Rozia

by

Marylou Bugh

Every life is a story — Marylou Bugh

Marylou Bugh
3404 Senske Rd
Standish, Michigan 48658
marylou.bugh@gmail.com

ISBN 978-0-692-24819-5

Printed in the United States of America

Dedicated to all of Rozia's family on the
other side of the curtain of life
And all who are still here continuing her story.

INTRODUCTION

The following is the life story of my mother, Rose Swiecicki Trombley. Unfortunately, she never had the chance to see the completed version before she left us in June of 2001 at 96½ years, but she put up with my 'interviews' that filled eight tapes. Although I have inserted a few Polish names that she would have used in her early years, I have kept most in English, as she did when telling me her story. Italicized text is research I did to add background or explanation that often Rozia herself added on hindsight.

I felt free to include items from the wider world in her story to ground the reader in time, although they were not necessarily included in Mom's recorded tapes. The inserted items are not random. Mom's position on politics, religion and the ethics of science were always clear. She read and listened to current events and, whenever family or neighbors gathered, she always provoked a lively discussion about the state of the world. In her last years, she planned to research and write historical events during her lifetime, although the only family history she actually wrote was an account for the Bay City Times when it ran a series of family stories in 1986. I've included it as an appendix.

Mom had a formidable intelligence, and this is not an idle statement. When I was earning my Masters, I had to give IQ (intelligence quotient) tests to every age group. Mom was my designated senior, and she put up with my assignment; she tested superior intelligence. When I was a teen, this was the woman that I thought didn't understand anything!

I was much more humble when I explained my tape recorder. When she knew my project, she cooperated with the same curiosity and enthusiasm that fueled much of her life, and she was as open and helpful as she could be. She could not and did not tell me her innermost feelings, and she may have wanted the tapes transcribed without embellishment. Although she loved to read, she read no fiction and tolerated none in her real life.

So forgive me, Mama, Rozia, for casting the stories you've remembered in a fictional format. Even if I've written your life in the way I've chosen, I did not invent any scenes. I guess the next generation will see your life through my imperfect lens. I love you and appreciate the life you have given to me– to us.

Marylou

And the perceived became the remembered,

The remembered, the perceived.

~ Louise Gluck

George and Josephine (Sczygiel) Swiecicki

I

She shivers and says she thinks the house
feels chilly, and puts more wood in the stove...
Time to plant tears says the almanac.

~ Elizabeth Bishop

The Michigan morning dawned late, sullen with gray clouds hanging where the sun should have been. "It might snow," Busia said. She peered out the kitchen window. "You have to hurry, George."

Rozia sat on the chair closest to the wood stove, but she could feel the December drafts chase across the kitchen floor. "I'm cold," she said.

Her grandmother looked at her, but Rozia could tell that Busia wasn't really listening, and Busia's eyes were red as if she had been crying. Tata, Rozia's daddy, bowed his head so far over his untouched oatmeal that she could see nothing of his face, only the top of his dark hair. Something had changed this morning, something deeper and sadder than the last weeks since Busia Swiecicki had come to cook and clean for them.

Rozia slid off her chair. "Mama?"

"Azia," Busia called her by the nickname she always used for Rozia, but Rozia didn't listen. She ran across the parlor floor to the front bedroom, and reached across the quilt and grasped the hand that had always stretched towards her when she came through the bedroom door.

"Mama!" Even before Rozia touched the cold hand, she knew that Mama would not answer. More than once in the last week,

Mama had told her that she would die soon, but that Rozia was not to be afraid or sad. Now that Rozia was a big girl, already seven, she would need to help Tata take care of the house and her three younger brothers. Mama promised that she would be watching from Heaven even if Rozia couldn't see her. When Mama had called Rozia into the bedroom last night, it was Mama's last kiss before she went to heaven.

"Azia, come now." Busia followed her and scooped her up away from the bed.

"Mama told me that anytime I want to, I can talk to her," Rozia said.

Busia's shoulders shook and her voice broke. "Yes, I'm sure she did. She was hardly past a child herself."

Busia was not talking right. Rozia knew that Mama was twenty-three, so Mama couldn't be a child if Rozia was seven and already a big girl. She wriggled out of Busia's arms. "I want to talk to her now."

"Yes– yes child, later." Busia searched her apron pocket for a handkerchief. She took Rozia's hand. "Come now and get dressed before your brothers get up. People will be here and wonder why you don't have your shoes on."

Yes, Mama would want her to be dressed when company came. Rozia followed Busia back to the kitchen. She only looked back once. How still and white Mama looked in the darkened room, and even under the heavy quilt, Mama's hand was cold.

Tata was putting on his great fur coat, the one he wore to town or church. His eyes, dark with sadness, looked almost black in his pale face. Rozia watched silently as he pulled down the fur hat over his ears and walked out the back door. Soon their wagon, pulled by Old Dan, bounced over the driveway's frozen ruts and down the road. Tata looked so cold and alone in the wagon seat.

"Where is Tata going?" Rozia asked.

"To get a casket," Busia answered shortly. "Come, help with the dishes."

The kitchen was dark with the December day, but it was the biggest and warmest place in the house. Rozia and her brothers always played under and around the big square table in the center of the room. The black cook stove with a cavernous oven, fueled from the woodpile outside the door, was kept going all day. Homemade shelves over the dry sink held dishes and kettles. But the pantry, adjacent to the kitchen stored the dried apples and corn, the crocks of side pork and pickles and sauerkraut, the beans and ground wheat and cornmeal. The pantry and the root cellar were well-stocked when December came, but it was the kitchen where everyone gathered, and it was the kitchen where Aunt Antoinette, who lived down the road, came today with her daughters, Angeline and Dora, Rozia's favorite cousins.

Anna Trombley, the neighbor from across the road, soon followed with a bread pudding. Rozia's mouth watered and she and Dora exchanged looks of happy expectation, but they knew enough to keep quiet. Anna looked sad and worried as she and Aunt Antoinette and Busia talked about Tata, alone on his sad trip, each reassuring the others that he wouldn't be long and there wouldn't be any big snow and Old Dan would come through any kind of weather to get back to his warm stall.

Rozia watched Anna Trombley's sad and worried face. Rozia remembered Mama and Tata talking about how Anna's husband climbed down from the barn roof he was building last June, lay down on the sofa with an awful headache and died the same day. A man that looked as strong as Doug Trombley should have lived another forty years. His casket had been carried to church on a horse-drawn wagon. Would Mama's casket leave the same way with

Old Dan pulling the wagon as sure and steady as the women said he was?

Angeline, who was a few years older than Rozia and Dora, ran from the kitchen to the road looking for Tata. Her round, young face streamed with tears. "You shouldn't cry, Angeline," Rozia told her cousin. "Mama's in heaven." Angeline just cried harder. Rozia thought that Angeline and Anna did not seem to understand about Heaven.

As the day wore on, Busia, Aunt Antoinette and Anna Trombley disappeared into the front bedroom. Tata had not yet arrived with the casket, so they brought Mama out to the parlor on boards. They had dressed her in the blue Sunday dress that she had not worn in some time, and they put pennies on her eyes to keep them closed and folded her hands across her chest with a rosary dangling from her white fingers. In spite of all the people in the house, Rozia remembered to kneel and say a 'Hail Mary'. Mama said it was important to pray.

Rozia's aunts and cousins bustled around the house during the wake, welcoming neighbors, accepting their food offerings, insisting that Tata eat, arranging a vigil so that someone sat by Mama day and night until the casket was loaded on the wagon, a box closed, unfamiliar. They buried Mama on December 23rd, 1908. That day, all the women dressed in sober colors with veils of mourning, and Tata wore a black arm band. At the grave, each mourner bent and scooped a handful of earth to throw on the casket as they sang "Barwo Swienti", "Saint Barbara, Pearl of Jesus". Their voices wavered between the mournful Polish hymn and the sobs that overcame them. Rozia watched and shook from the cold December wind. She didn't cry. She imagined that Heaven was warm and pretty like a spring day. Heaven would not be like a Michigan December.

After the funeral, Tata brought Busia back to the house. He took off his black arm band, sank down by the kitchen table, and put his hands over his face. His sobs filled the empty room. "My Josie. She's gone," he sobbed.

Busia stood over him and scolded, "Stop that! Your Josie is in a better place." She grabbed a kitchen towel and mopped her own tears and then his. "Stop that now. Are you crazy?"

Rozia looked around the cold, bleak kitchen that had been full of relatives and neighbors in the last few days. She thought of Mama making potato pancakes and singing Polish songs while Tata carried in the wood and whistled an accompaniment. When Mama started coughing, the Polish songs about lovers in the woods and the potato pancakes stopped. One evening when Mama was coming in from milking, Tata had to carry her into the house. She coughed up a dishpan of blood, and Rozia remembered the trail of blood from the barn that she had seen in the snow. Mama's in heaven Rozia whispered to herself, but it didn't comfort her the way it had the first time she said it.

❧ ❧ ❧

The day before Christmas, Tata's sister, Rozia's Aunt Tillie, came to the house, her arms full of brown-paper packages. Her hands trembled as she put them on the kitchen table and looked at Busia.

"These are for the kids from"– She hesitated. "From their mother."

Busia stared at Tillie, and Aunt Tillie's voice shook. "When I was here last, she gave me money and told me what to buy for them. She told me to hurry." Aunt Tillie was crying now, tears streaming down her small face. "She wanted to give them the presents herself. I should have come sooner, but I didn't think"–

Busia pulled one of the packages across the table and looked in. "What did you think? That consumption hangs around forever?"

She handed a package to Rozia. "From your mama, Azia. Bring your brothers here. They have something too." But Rozia forgot about her brothers as she opened the package and took out a flaxen-haired doll dressed in pink with a pink bow in her hair.

"Oh!" she breathed. "I was Mama's dolly, and now I'm the mama of a dolly. I'm going to keep her forever."

Busia and Aunt Tilly looked at her and Busia wore a small frown. She hoped this girl was not a little too fanciful for her own good. "Go get your brothers," she said shortly.

Busia Swiecicki stayed on after the funeral, but soon enough, she scolded Tata. "You better find yourself a wife. I'm not going to take care of your kids forever." Grandma's words were not meant to be unkind, but she was a woman brusque in manner and after raising eleven children of her own and losing her husband three years ago to typhoid, she had already had a long, hard life.

❧ ❧ ❧

Rozia's Grandmother Swiecicki was born Katarzyna Drzewicki. Her father, Con Drzewicki, was listed as a Prussian in German-occupied Poland, and Katarzyna grew up in a world that seethed and talked about having a free country. In the Koldrab, Znin area of Poland, she had been a nurse for the wounded during one of Poland's interminable wars when she met and married the Bohemian Joseph Ciaciuch in 1866. After he had fathered two children, he went off to war and never came back.

Katarzyna went to work as a servant girl in the home of a land holder who could afford the luxury of hired help. It was there she met Frank Swiecicki, the son of another servant on the estate and the illegitimate son of the lord himself. The man kept and supported the unfortunate servant girl, but Frank was really no more than a servant himself. In 1870 Katarzyna married Rozia's Grandpa Frank. He carried the surname of his father (which, oddly enough translates 'holy' or 'saintly'), but now that he was grown, his name was no guarantee that he would not be drafted into the military service. Although Katarzyna still had a picture of her first love with gun and sabre, she was afraid of losing another husband to Poland's wars.

Frank came to America and eventually earned passage for Katarzyna and their children. Rozia's Tata, George, was eleven years old when he and his stepbrothers and siblings came to America. Katarzyna didn't know their passage included meals and fed her children bread and water.

George Swiecicki and his second wife, Agnes Wrzenski

II

My heart lifted up with the great grasses;
The weeds believed me, and the nesting birds.

~ Theodore Roethke

In the months after Mama's funeral, Busia stayed on and cooked and scrubbed and kept the stack of cotton diapers washed, but she relied on Rosia to watch over toddler Vick and baby Joe who now crept all over and pulled himself up by chairs and table legs, which gave Vick the perfect opportunity to push him over. Vick had to be watched every minute he was awake. Rozia tried to keep her voice patient and low like Mama did when Vick tipped his cup of milk over for the third time or baby Joe filled his diaper ten minutes after she had changed him, or Walt tracked mud in, but she was no match for her three brothers. She didn't want to be the big girl anymore.

Tata married Agnes Wrzesinski in May of 1909, a few months after Grandma Swiecicki's warning. He was thirty-five, a widower with four young children and a reluctant live-in mother. Agnes Wrzesinski was eighteen and lived with her mother in a big farmhouse across the section. They went to the same church. That's all Tata knew about her. But Rozia welcomed the prospect of a stepmother, someone who would lift the gloom that had fallen over their house. Tata might sing his Polish songs again and a new woman in the house might take away the worried frown from Tata's face.

And so Rozia enjoyed Tata's small wedding. The supper table was loaded with beans and ham and chicken and, best of all, a wedding cake that Agnes's mother, the new Busia, had made. After the wedding feast, the men rolled back the rug on the parlor floor and the new stepmother's brother pulled out the first strains of sound from an accordion. Music! The new Busia was dressed in a wide Polish skirt and her feet flew as fast as the player's fingers across the keys of the accordion. Her colorful skirt whirled around her, a bright pinwheel. Rozia watched in awe as she danced with first one man and then another.

"She can dance the feet off any man," Rozia heard Anna Trombley remark to Aunt Antoinette. "She married and buried three." Rozia was fascinated with the new busia who had survived three marriages and could still dance like the wind. Maybe the new busia would sew Rozia a skirt that whirled like a pinwheel and teach her to dance. It seemed life had changed with this new family that had come into her life.

The summer after Tata's wedding, Rozia played house in the toilet when she went to visit the new busia. Stepmother's oldest sister was deaf and dumb and had never found a husband, so she stayed home and kept the place so clean that even the outside toilet was spotless. The new busia seemed to like Rozia and her brothers. At least she didn't expect Rozia to watch her brothers when they visited. The toilet was a quiet spot and had catalogues that Rozia liked to look at and imagine a house decorated with all the catalogues had to offer. The small place became a grand mansion, a castle until the visit was over and she followed stepmother back home.

Rozia found out that summer that no one in this new family could read. Her stepmother's brother took his lunch pail and went to school until he was sixteen and never got past the first reader. Rozia found it puzzling that they weren't good with school. She was well past the easy readers, although her first school year hadn't gone well.

When she started Oxbow School, Mama was still alive and worried about Rozia's first day. Rozia was only four years old and couldn't speak English.

"What will she do if she has to go to the toilet?" Mama asked Tata. He knew more English than she did.

Tata instructed Rozia, "Say 'I have to go pee.'"

"No! No!" Mama said in alarm when she heard the translation. "That is too crude. Tell her how to say "I have to go out." Although Tata spoke enough English to get around, he often didn't know the polite way to say things as Mama would have.

(Since Rozia's father had come from the part of Poland taken over by Germany, he spoke low Polish that mixed German words with their native tongue. Rozia's mother had been born in Bay County, and although she didn't know what part of Poland her family had come from, her Polish was high Polish, which was the more formal version, unmixed with other languages).

As it was, Mama and Tata's instruction helped little. Rozia's first teacher, Miss Maude, did not like the ways of her young charges, these children from parents just off the boat. "Jar, jar, jar," she sneered. "Their language is jar, jar, jar." She rapped her students' hands with a ruler every time they lapsed into their native tongue.

One day Henry Jankowski, one of the older boys, had enough. When he tried to leave, Miss Maude locked him in the schoolhouse, and he broke a window and ran away. Rozia was in awe of such misbehavior, but Henry's father probably never told him how to behave. Rozia and her brother, Walter, often stood by their gate and watched Henry's father half stagger, half crawl his way home from Lixey's Corner. His wayward progress often took him through the mud and close to the ditch. When it was swollen from the spring rains, Rozia worried that he might fall in and drown. But he never did. Rozia and Walter never laughed at Henry's father. Tata had told them more than once that it was wrong to laugh at people. "Judge not lest you be judged," he told them. "Everybody is different."

But Rozia learned little that first year of school, except to say as little as possible. After her first chart year, as the beginners were called, she went to St. Valentine's, a school that the church held for Polish kids. At Saint Valentines, she quickly learned not only reading and math but her catechism.

Maybe Stepmother's family never went to St. Valentine's. She already knew how it felt to say as little as possible in school. Everybody was different, and Stepmother's brothers were good workers and one could play the accordion without ever reading music notes like the teacher did.

And the new busia knew how to grow a garden. One day she came across the section with a large syrup can full of peas she had just picked. Rozia was on the front porch and Busia plunked the can down in front of her and went into the kitchen to gossip with Stepmother. Rozia's mouth watered at the full green pods. She had just taken her first bite when Walt came up to the porch from the wood pile, still carrying his little axe. He was a year younger than Rozia, but he was always trying to act like Tata, trying to be the big man.

"Oh boy! Peas! Give me some," he commanded.

"No. Busia gave them to me," Rozia said, hugging the pail close.

"No she didn't. Give me some, Azia."

Rozia only held the pail tighter. She hated to be bossed.

Walt looked from his sister's stubborn face to her bare feet on the wooden steps. "Give me some or I'll cut your toes off," he said.

"No," she said.

The axe flashed through the air so fast, Rozia didn't even have time to flinch. They both looked in horrified wonder at her little toe, so deeply gashed, it hung from her foot by a shred of skin. Blood spurted out staining the wooden steps.

Still clutching the metal pail, Rozia screamed, "My toe! My toe! You cut off my toe!"

Tata came around the corner of the woodshed and Walt jumped down from the porch and ran. Tata ignored him and picked up Rozia and went quickly into the house. He grabbed a dishpan and plunged her foot into water from the teakettle, then wrapped a clean rag around it and pressed the toe back, binding it tightly while the women looked on in horror.

"He cut off my toe!" Rozia sobbed.

"Stop your crying," Tata ordered. "You still have your toe."

Rozia gulped down her sobs as the blood stopped its flow. Walt eventually got his spanking, but that was not what comforted Rozia. Tata had saved her. Rozia sat on the porch the rest of the afternoon eating fresh peas. If Tata hadn't been there, Stepmother wouldn't have known what to do. Stepmother played in the fields with Rozia and Walt, throwing clods of dirt and giggling like a young girl. Rozia liked it that Stepmother didn't care if Rozia put on her shoes or combed her hair. When Busia Swiecicki lived with them, Grandma's clothes were always clean and starched and she wore her hair parted in the middle and drawn back in a neat bun. She never played or giggled, and she expected Rozia to keep her hair and clothes as straight her own. Rozia got tired of being told to act like a lady.

But Busia Swiecicki would have known what to do with a toe that was half cut off. The new Busia wouldn't and Stepmother wouldn't either. When they visited the new Busia and Rozia hid in the toilet inventing her imaginary castle and they got ready to leave, usually baby Joe needed a diaper change and often Vick had bumps and scrapes. Rozia felt a gnaw of worry.

Mike Ciaciuch holding granddaughter, Rozia's brother Joe,
Tony Ciaciuch, Dora Ciaciuch and Rozia's Grandmother Swiecicki

III

O for a touch of a vanished hand,
And the sound of a voice that is still.

~ Tennyson

When Rozia's father and his step brother, Mike Ciachuch bought their farms, Beaver Township was just coming into its own. Ten miles west and five miles north of Bay City, the township (35.4 sq. miles) was officially recognized in 1867, the fifth such in Bay County and, at first, it had little to recommend it. Levi Willard, the first township supervisor, held township elections in his home. In 1873 there were only fifty families living in the still heavily wooded area on the north branch of the Kawkawlin River. German settlers who had ventured into the area, described the 60,000 acres that the government had bought from the Chippewa, as a land of forest denser than the Black Forest.

However after 1844, when the first sawmill was built on the Kawkawlin (the Chippewa name for 'place of pike fish'), lumbering was changing the face of the land. The river was soon filled with more logs than pike, and the Chippewa's way of life on the river was gone.

When it became obvious that the cleared land was excellent farm land, the newly-formed township grew rapidly, and the government sold the cleared land for $1.25 an acre. In 1880, there were 350 residents, by 1894 there were 1,236 and by 1900, 1,539. Land prices rose to $75 an acre. Even though lumbering was still a part of the township's income, Beaver Township had become a community of small farms, owned by Polish and German immigrants who were familiar with *the crops that grew best in a climate that was not that different from Poland and Germany.*

Tata and his brother had arranged that one would work for a weekly wage and one would stay and manage the farms. Tata was the brother who would work away. He was gone all week working in the lumber mills or working in the salt mines; jobs were not that hard to find.

His stepbrother, Mike Ciahuch, took care of the big farm work, such as the plowing and planting and butchering or selling livestock, but the day-to-day jobs--feeding the animals, milking the cows, churning the butter, making cottage cheese, tending and harvesting the garden—were left to Stepmother. Rozia's father expected his young wife to care for things as his first wife had done and his mother had done, but four young children and constant farm work was more than his new wife could handle. She was expected to gain control of something that was not in her control at all, and Rozia was the first to suffer the consequences.

As the pressure of keeping up a farmhouse and four children increased, Stepmother's field play stopped, and Rozia learned another side of her. When things went wrong, it was Rozia's fault. Perhaps it was the flash of disbelief in Rozia's eyes when she heard Stepmother and her mother tell their stories. Perhaps it was because Rozia was the oldest and the only girl in the family that Stepmother had inherited, a girl that carried the look and the ways of the woman Stepmother could not replace. Rozia was slapped, punched and kicked, she who had been her young mother's dolly, who had never gotten more than a swat on her butt. Rozia shrank more into herself. She didn't tell Tata on his visits home. She must be doing something wrong. She was supposed to be the big girl, not a whiner. The more she tried to make it right, the more often she was hit.

❧ ❧ ❧

One day, when Stepmother left to visit her mother, Rozia was busy at the sink, scrubbing the pots clean. She risked a peek out of the narrow kitchen window to see her stepmother's short figure emerging past the tool shed into the field beyond. At least she could get the work done without a punch or a kick. Stepmother would visit for quite a while, and Rozia was happy for the time alone, mistress of the house.

During the past year, Rozia had learned that her stepmother and the new busia filled their lives with superstition and folklore that sounded as full of fancy as fairy tales with bad endings, stories of witches and hexes and marked babies. When Stepmother told Tata the stories, he forbade her to listen or repeat any more of such nonsense. "You can't serve God and mammon both," he said. But when Tata was gone, Stepmother would visit her mother and listen to the strange tales as if it was truth.

Rozia turned from the kitchen window and crept to the pantry. Stepmother was drawn to the strange and frightening stories just as Rozia was drawn to the cake Stepmother had put up on the shelf this morning. All of her brothers were tucked away for their naps except Walter who was playing on the woodpile and would stay out there all afternoon. All she would do is take a little frosting that had drizzled down on the plate, just a little with her finger. She was no dummy. She wouldn't risk Stepmother's wrath by taking a whole piece, but who would notice if the edge of the plate was licked clean?

Stepmother had baked the cake for Tata's weekend home. Rozia looked forward to Tata's times at home and not only because Stepmother did not hit and kick when he was around. Tata had stories too, new things happening that often sounded as unreal as fairy tales except these stories came from newspapers and newspapers had real stories; like the one about a couple of brothers who had invented a machine that flew for thirty miles. Tata said he wouldn't ever try to fly. A big balloon called the Zeppelin that carried people through the air like a magic carpet had caught on fire and everybody burned to death. "Some things should be left alone," Tata said.

The cake was on one of the highest shelves. On tiptoe, Rozia felt along the rim of the plate and her fingers touched the sweet, sticky goo. Her mouth watered. Such a treat after potatoes and bread, bread and potatoes, side pork and potatoes, cabbage and potatoes. When she became a lady, her kitchen would never see a potato and the bread would be soft and white, not heavy brown bread.

Her finger rubbed harder on the plate, and suddenly without warning, the plate tipped and fell upside down. Rozia stared in horror at the overturned cake lying at her feet as neat as if it was planned. She couldn't fix it no matter how hard she would try. Stepmother would grab her by the hair and shake her like a dust rag, fling her against the wall, and yell that she was a stupid, clumsy girl to ruin the cake for Tata's coming-home weekend.

A sob tore Rozia's throat and then another, ripping the silence of the dim pantry. How could she explain, who could she tell that she didn't mean to ruin Tata's cake?

She ran to the living room to the picture of the Blessed Mother Mary. "Mama," she sobbed out loud, "would you talk to Blessed Mother and Jesus? Tell them I didn't mean to hurt anything. I was just going to lick the frosting"-- She stopped as sobs overtook her. "I try to be good, Mama. I do. I didn't mean"--

She felt someone in the room and turned. Stepmother stood in the doorway, her eyes still squinted from the sun outside. Rozia's sobs stopped and she got off her knees. Her legs felt weak as if they wouldn't hold her, but she stood and looked at the floor waiting for the first blow. She wouldn't cry anymore. She just wanted the beating and the name calling over with.

Stepmother stared at Rozia a minute and then turned and went to the pantry and with one deft swoop of her short, strong hands, she flipped the cake back on the plate and up on the shelf. It was crooked and smeared but mostly intact. Then she walked out of the kitchen door without a word.

Rozia lifted her head and looked around the room. Mama and Mother Mary had kept Stepmother's cruel hand stilled. Mama would be there anytime Rozia needed her.

Rozia, far right, with cousins Dora and Tony Ciaciuch

IV

Whom I began to think and call my own.
Farewell, too little, and too lately known,

~ John D

In spite of Rozia's prayers, her stepmother's resentment did not cease in the following months, and Rozia had almost accepted it, although she had confronted Stepmother once. It was just after milking time and Rozia was on her way to the milk house. She had to clean the separator, a hand-turned machine that separated the milk from the cream. The cream was saved and sold to the local cheese factory, and the skim milk given to the pigs. The separator had several parts and a multitude of disks had to be cleaned after each milking. It was a job that Rozia hated. She walked slowly up the path, her eyes on the sloshing tin pail of water she carried. The milk house had a flowing well, but that water was too cold.

Suddenly, Stepmother rounded the corner of the barn with the pail of whole milk they kept out for their own use. She stepped in front of Rozia and spit at her. Rozia wiped the spit from her face, and anger exploded in her as she had never felt before. She pulled up the pail of water and threw it in Stepmother's face. As quickly as this new, raw feeling of anger overwhelmed Rozia, it disappeared and she cringed in fear, waiting for the stinging punishment that she surely deserved. "Honor thy Father and Mother", she had learned from her catechism. Stepmother, for better or worse, was her mother now, and Rozia had just done the unthinkable. But Stepmother continued up the path as if the encounter had never happened. Rozia stared at her retreating figure, as frightened by Stepmother's lack of reaction as she was of her own hot anger. She whispered a little prayer to Mother Mary and resolved she would never do such a thing again.

Shortly after that, Rozia learned that Stepmother was going to have a baby. Baby Joe was just out of diapers. Rozia had learned to pick up women's talk when they didn't know she was listening. At any rate, it would have taken someone blind and deaf to miss Stepmother's change from the clump-throwing, giggling girl when she first married, or even the sharply resentful stepmother, to the terrified woman who sat by the stove clutching her stomach. The stories that Stepmother's mother had told and Tata had discounted as superstitious nonsense had left their mark. Stepmother thought she was going to die. Her first baby was stillborn. The next baby lived a few weeks. The neighbor women dressed baby Frankie in a dress that one of Rozia's aunts had made. The summer heat was too intense that year for a proper mourning, and they laid the tiny coffin in the pantry, the coolest place in the house.

Rozia took on more and more of the household work. The flaxen-haired doll, her last gift from her mother, had long since been broken by her brother Vick who had discovered its hiding place under her bed. Rozia cried in the barn where no one could see her tears. What foolishness to cry over a doll, she tried to scold herself. She had little time for playing Mama with a doll.

Her next tears were harder to hide, and the green potato plants blurred as she kept stopping to look across the field toward Uncle Mike's house. Aunt Antoinette was dying. Why did Tata keep her out here in the field picking potato bugs? Uncle Mike Ciacuch was Tata's stepbrother, but Aunt Antoinette was Rozia's own mother's sister. Uncle and Auntie were doubly-related. Why couldn't Rozia be with her aunt and Dora and Angeline? Aunt Antoinette always made Rozia feel safe and happy when she walked to Uncle Mike's to play house with Dora. Their favorite game was dressing like ladies from a barrel of clothes. Those times were gone now, but the memories were doubly precious. Aunt Antoinette's house had almost felt like Mama. Rozia's house didn't feel like Mama at all anymore, but she couldn't tell her aunt that her new stepmother was not like Mama.

Perhaps Aunt Antoinette had guessed. When Rozia made her First Communion in May, Aunt Antoinette was the one who found Rozia a white communion dress and veil. Then she took Rozia along with Dora and Dora's brother, Theodore, to a studio in Bay City to have their picture taken.

"A waste of money," Tata had grumbled.

"This is a special time, George," Auntie had insisted. "Sometimes money needs to be spent to make a time special."

Tata had given in to his sister-in-law. He must have seen that Antoinette already had the dreaded consumption. Her face was gaunt, and she had the cough. The day they went to the studio, she wore her best Sunday dress. "It will be a special time for me too," Aunt Antoinette told the kids. "I'm going to have my picture taken, so all of you will have something to remember me by."

For all of Aunt Antoinette's efforts to make Rozia's Holy Communion special, it had done little to curb Stepmother's strange behavior that day. When the mothers served dinner to the first communicants at the church, Stepmother snatched bowls of food as quickly as possible from the others and loaded Rozia's plate, not talking to the other women at all, but working in a silent frenzy. Rozia had looked around to see if others noticed. Stepmother's behavior seemed especially strange to Rozia, since at home Stepmother never loaded Rozia's plate at all. Rozia remembered little else of that meal, except that she ate as quickly as she could. She just wanted to go home.

Now Rozia looked at the house across the field again, and tears spilled down her cheeks. She hadn't realized that Aunt Antoinette already knew that First Communion day that she would also die of the dreaded consumption that had taken Mama.

When Tata came into the field where Rozia was working, his tall figure cast a long shadow in the rays of the dying sun. Tata wasn't one to say much about how he felt, but Rozia could see the sadness in his long face and in the way his mouth turned down under his thick moustache. Rozia's last link with her mother was gone.

Aunt Antoinette was already laid out in their parlor when Rozia and Stepmother took a cake to the house. Rozia knelt and said a 'Hail Mary', but seeing the tears of her cousins, she cried for their mother and for her own that she missed more than ever. Both might be in Heaven, but Heaven was a long ways away. They buried Aunt Antoinette in 1911 in much the same way as they had buried Mama.

V

And father walked over the wide garnered acres
Where a cutting wind warned him of the cold to come.

~ Sterling A. Brown

Stepmother's third baby, Delphine, lived for eight months and died in Rozia's arms one chilly autumn afternoon while Tata walked the fields with Stepmother. Stepmother's unreasoning fears of the unknown had not abated, and Tata kept her away from her kitchen corner as often as possible. He took her out of the house and drove her to the neighbors or sat her under a tree while he did the fieldwork.

Rozia tried her best to help Stepmother take care of this little sister, but nothing had helped. Maybe Rozia hadn't prayed hard enough. Maybe she hadn't heard Delphine's weak cries during the night. Rozia's arms felt crushed by the baby's limp body, and sorrow ripped through her at the sight of the tiny face, now still and waxen as a doll's. She couldn't cry. She was a big girl now, almost eleven years old. Mama had told her she had to help Tata, and crying wouldn't help Tata.

After Delphine's death, Baby Leo survived, but Stepmother's condition worsened. She threw herself on the bed in hysterical fits of laughing and shaking. Tata had to quit his job out of town, a blow to the arrangement between him and Uncle Mike. Tata's outside jobs paid the taxes and the payments on their farms, but it was obvious that he needed to be home for more than weekends. Rozia had no idea of the cost of the new arrangement without the money Tata had earned outside of farming. She was just happy to have her father home.

One afternoon Doctor Herrick stopped in with his wife. He stopped in quite often now. Mrs. Herrick sat down by the kitchen table while the doctor went into the parlor with Tata.

"How are you doing, Rose?" she asked, calling Rozia by her English name.

"Fine," Rozia said, scooping the dishes off the table from a dinner of cabbage, potatoes and side pork. She felt uncomfortable around the doctor's wife. The baby scooted between Rozia's legs and almost tripped her.

In the uncomfortable silence, she heard Doctor Herrick's voice rise. "George, she's not going to get any better. You have to send her to Traverse City. There's an asylum there for the insane. It's–"

"How can I send her to an asylum?" Tata's voice was loud. "I've got a houseful of kids."

"God, man, look at the woman. Rose is doing everything, and she's a kid herself. You've got a problem, and it's not going to get any better. They will take good care of Agnes there."

Mrs. Herrick scooped up the baby and bounced him on her knee. Rozia hoped his diaper was dry.

"Rose, see this on the baby's head?"

Rozia's face flamed. "I tried to scrub it off, Mrs. Herrick. I wash him. I do."

"It's cradle cap. Lots of babies have it." Mrs. Herrick took a jar of Vaseline out of her purse. "The next time you wash him, rub this into his hair. Do that a few times and it will go away."

Rozia nodded and mopped the table. She wanted to hear what was going on in the parlor, but the men's voices had fallen to a low rumble.

Mrs. Herrick fished a bright-colored ball out of her big purse. She put the baby down with the toy and rolled up her sleeves to help Rozia with the dishes. Rozia was too embarrassed to do more than get the dishes done and wish her gone.

Doctor Herrick and Tata took Stepmother to Traverse City the following week. Rozia only knew that the insane asylum might fix Stepmother, and that was something neither she nor Tata knew how to do.

❧ ❧ ❧

The Traverse City asylum had opened in 1885, the third in the state, and under Dr. James Munson's supervision, it had rapidly expanded to include twelve housing cottages and two infirmaries. Dr.Munson was a man who believed that beauty is therapy, and the grounds were planted with a variety of trees and flowers. Strait jackets were forbidden and work therapy was a large part of the asylum's philosophy. Rozia's stepmother was not harshly treated, but the huge complex must have been terrifying to her, and her stay did little to relieve her strange and disturbing fears. In 1913, little was known about hormonal imbalance or clinical depression, and none of the modern medications were available for hundreds of women who were sent to Traverse City. Many may not have been mentally ill, but suffering from ignorance, complicated by rapid pregnancies and burdened with physical work they could not handle. Neither Tata nor Rozia ever knew the exact cause of stepmother's 'nervous breakdown'.

❧ ❧ ❧

At first, Tata did his best to put up with the humiliation that had befallen his home. Insane asylums were for crazy people, and no family wanted to admit that theirs was touched by insanity. He bought a hand-operated wringer, so it would be easier for Rozia to do the laundry, and he tried to visit Stepmother, but Traverse City was across the state, and he had neither the money nor the time to live with this altered state of affairs. After a few months, over the doctor's objections, Tata brought Stepmother back home.

Rozia heard him tell their neighbor, Anna Trombley, "How can they help her there? She sees these terrible things the women are doing to each other. It's worse than if she was at home."

Anna shook her head sadly. Her own mother, trying to deal with eleven children, baking a dozen loaves of bread in an outside oven and washing heavy work clothes on a washboard, had no escape. Her legs curled so she could not walk and her speech garbled until the day she died. No one recognized that Anna's mother was also afflicted by a mental condition. She was just an unfortunate invalid, and Anna had to help her father and brother, Theodore, take care of her mother much as Rozia had to help Tata now.

Rozia remembered one time when she and Beattie cut across John Nowak's field to go to school. Mr. Nowak (Anna's dad) told them they could pick up all the apples they wanted that lay in the orchard. She could still hear the incessant rapping of Anna's mother's stick inside, the only way she communicated. She had seen the girls picking apples and wanted them gone. At least Stepmother wasn't a total invalid. Maybe that insane asylum had done some good after all.

VI

The spider unwinds a thread of her devising:
A thin, premeditated rig
To use in rising.

~ E.B. White

In spite of the increasing burden at home, Rozia managed to go to school, although she often missed days and even weeks. But after Tata was back home, he sent her and her brothers in the winter months, even though it often meant their farm chores waited until the school day was over.

After Rozia had learned her catechism well enough at St. Valentine's to receive her First Communion, she went to Cherry School. St. Valentine's taught Polish-speaking children how to read and write, but Cherry School went all the way to eighth grade, something St. Valentine's could not do, and Tata said an education in English was a necessity in America.

Although Rozia had certainly attended St. Valentine's School in the early 1900's, the St. Valentine's school that celebrated sixty-one years of existence before it recently closed, opened in 1948. The original school was built before St. Valentine's church. At the time, it seems the school's mission was not only to teach Polish-speaking children their Catholic catechism, but a working knowledge of English, and a general education so they could learn in the public schools.

Only a couple of miles separated the one-room Oxbow and Cherry schools, but both operated simultaneously for several years. Possibly both were needed because of the large families that populated the area. One year, Cherry School held 78 children.

Fifth from left in first row, Beatrice Trombley;
Rozia, top row, second from the end on the right.

School always started with the Pledge to the flag and songs to the accompaniment of the school organ. On cold days they all marched around the classroom until the room was warm enough to sit at their lessons, and Rozia learned the unfamiliar songs, one phrase at a time.

She had learned to read and do math at St. Valentine's but after her bad experience at Oxbow, Rozia went to Cherry School fearing the worst. But soon enough, she found that Miss McDonald, the teacher at Cherry school, was as different from Miss Maude as an apple is different from a potato. Miss McDonald was gentle and encouraged students with prizes for best reader, best anything. Rozia's grades soared. When she was in fourth grade, her math was so good that Miss McDonald asked her to help the other fourth graders.

By the end of fifth grade, Rozia had read every book in the small library housed in a kitchen cabinet in the corner of the classroom and won best reader prizes. Captivated by a book about Fusca, a mother ant and her underground home, Rozia amused her younger brothers by sitting on the floor and spinning similar stories about the spider who wove a web in the corner of their kitchen doorway. And she could help Tata with letters that were written in English. Now she could read English better than he could. Tata was proud of her, and Rozia was proud that she could help him. Her school days were her brightest times.

But it was Miss Lindsey, her sixth grade teacher, that Rozia loved the most. Miss Lindsey was as soft-spoken as Miss McDonald, but she tolerated no nonsense from the big boys in her class, although many were bigger than she was. She took on Vern Evert, a new kid who scared the kids every recess with his threats and bullying. "You will get your work done in my classroom and leave the other students alone," she told him in no uncertain terms.

Vern just sneered, "That's what all the other schools told me. That's why my ma shipped me to Grandma's. Nothing's worked on me yet."

When it seemed Vern might have gotten the upper hand, two men walked into the classroom and took Vern off to reform school. Rozia clapped in relief with the rest of the class, and Elsie Krieger walked up and hugged Miss Lindsey. Rozia would have liked to hug Miss Lindsey, but hugging wasn't something her family did with anyone except babies.

"We're so glad he's gone," Elsie said.

Rozia felt the ugly pangs of envy. Miss Lindsey boarded at Elsie's, Elsie with her shiny shoes and frilly dresses. On the way home from school, Rozia said to Beattie Trombley, "You like Elsie Krieger, don't you?" Beatrice, the youngest of Anna Trombley's four children, never seemed to feel she wasn't as good as anyone else, or that nobody liked her. Rozia wished she could be more like Beattie, the neighborhood's name for her.

"She's nice," Beattie said. "I like how she hugged Miss Lindsey."

"I think Elsie's stuck up," Rozia said. "She goes trip, trip, trip with her fancy shoes, like she's so good."

Beattie laughed. "She invited me to stay overnight, and she said to bring a friend, so I'm going to bring you."

Rozia forgot her feelings of envy. "Oh Beattie! That would be so much fun."

Beattie looked back down the road. "Speaking of friends, here comes yours."

Rozia's gaze followed Beattie's. Oh no, Rozia thought when she saw Verna Jankowski hurrying towards them.

"I'll see you later," Beattie said and hurried to catch up to her older sister, Gert and her friends.

Verna flung her arm around Rozia's shoulders. "I was looking for you, Rozia," she said. "It's not fun to walk home alone. I'm glad you're my friend."

Rozia looked at the others ahead. Beattie thought Rozia liked Verna and her idle chatter. Verna never fit with the others, and somehow she had latched on to Rozia, maybe because Rozia felt that she didn't quite fit either. She resigned herself to putting up with Verna the rest of the walk home. It would be cruel to shake her off.

The only two things Rozia would remember of Elsie's invitation was the German fried potatoes that Elsie's mother made, a dish that Rozia had never tasted before, and loved ever after, and a realization that, just because Elsie wore nice clothes and Miss Lindsey boarded at their place, Elsie was not stuck up at all.

The only other girl that seemed to like Rozia besides Beattie was Barbara Buechler. Barbara's dad owned the sawmill, and Beattie and Rozia had cut across their woods more than once to pick violets for the teacher. Barbara's mother baked for the sawmill hands and gave the girls big slabs of homemade bread and buttermilk after school. Barbara was quite like Beattie in her easy disposition. Verna was nothing like Barbara or Beattie. Verna was like a burr, clinging to Rozia, and Rozia didn't know how to shake off the needy girl's attention without hurting her. "Judge not lest you shall be judged," Rozia's dad had said. Sometimes it was hard.

VII

...I bruise and blunder,
break faith, leave ill enough
alone...

~ Adrienne Rich

Cherry School ended the year as it did every spring with a program and a box social. Girls brought decorated boxes with a lunch for two packed inside. These would be auctioned off to the highest bidder, who not only had a tempting lunch, but also the company of the young lady who made it. To add to the fun, the ones who bid on the brightly decorated concoctions didn't know whose box it was until after they won it. Of course, as often as not, word about who decorated which was whispered around.

In other years, Rozia paid little attention to the box social since it was for the big girls, but this year she was one of the big girls. Rozia knew that the box social brought money to Cherry School for extra books, but she had no inclination to be the focus of attention. One school program at the end of her chart year, Rozia wore Tata's huge fur coat and sang "I am the Robber Baron". She still remembered how upset she had been at the audience's screams of laughter.

But Beattie pulled her into getting ready for the day. As they fixed their boxes together at Beattie's, Beattie was full of conjecture about which boys would bid on their offerings.

"Will you really eat your lunch with Stanley if he buys your box?" Rozia asked, sticking another piece of fried chicken in their boxes. Lucky for them, Anna had chicken left over from Sunday dinner.

"Of course I will. And I know someone is interested in what your box will look like too."

"Oh no, Beattie! Who?"

Beattie's brown eyes danced. "I'm not telling."

"I don't want anyone but Tata buying my box," Rozia muttered, more apprehensive than ever.

"You're silly," Beattie said. "You know it's the young guys who buy the boxes. Your dad is not going to bid on your box."

The May day of the program dawned bright, and robins and wrens caroled from the trees all the way to school. It was a great day to be alive. Miss Lindsey was grateful for Rozia and Beattie's early appearance and put them to work setting up a table in the best section of the schoolyard under the elm tree and arranging the offerings as the other girls arrived with boxes decorated with ribbon and buttons and beads of every color. As apprehensive as she felt, Rozia couldn't help but notice how pretty the display looked.

The whole neighborhood turned out for the occasion. The older neighbors watched with amusement as the boxes were bid on and handed out amid squeals and blushes from the young ladies and swaggers from the young men. When Miss Lindsey finally held up Rozia's box, decorated with pink and white crepe paper, Rozia felt her face grow hot. What if no one bid on it? Verna's box went unbidden and Mr. Ratajcyck bought it to the laughter and cheers of the neighbors.

Rozia was surprised to hear from the back, "Ten cents."

"Twenty-five cents," someone responded.

"Thirty-five cents," the first voice countered.

Rozia was afraid to look around and see who was bidding. When her box finally went for fifty cents, the noisy audience cheered and clapped when Joe Gorsky walked up to claim his prize.

"I'm not going to eat with Joe Gorsky," Rozia fumed to Beattie, who sat next to her, serene in the knowledge that Stanley had bid sixty cents for her box.

Beattie turned and giggled, "You better, Rozia. Some little birdie told him whose box that was."

"You didn't!"

"I never said I did now, did I?"

When the bidding was over and the buyers and sellers found places around the yard and in the trees to sit with their feast, Rozia hid in the schoolroom that was set up for the afternoon's entertainment. The desks had all been pushed against the walls and extra chairs brought in for the neighborhood audience.

Out the window, Rozia saw Joe finally sit under the elm tree and open the pink and white box by himself. She felt terrible watching him, but she couldn't sit with him. She hardly knew him. What could she say? What would he say? She just couldn't.

The day was a long one. After the lunch and entertainment, there was an ice cream social and, for once, Rozia was almost happy for Verna's clinging company. When the shadows were long and the birds were singing their evening song, people began to drift away.

"Stanley's walking me home," Beattie said as they helped Miss Lindsey put the schoolroom back in order. Rozia could tell from her tone that she was not happy with the way Rozia had acted. Rozia nodded without comment. She would walk home by herself then. Even Verna had already left.

But on the schoolhouse steps, Casimir Stodlowski, approached her. He was a big, burly young man, already out of school. "Can I walk you home?" he asked.

Rozia was taken aback. Why would Casimir want to walk her home? She hardly knew him.

"I bid on your box too," he said.

"All right," she agreed. Perhaps it would atone for her rude behavior to poor Joe, who had disappeared from the festivities as soon as possible.

They followed Beattie and Stanley, and Rozia watched them enviously. They were singing songs from the entertainment, their voices floating back in a surprisingly good duet, occasionally punctuated with a burst of laughter. They seemed to be having a lot of fun.

Casimir talked little.

"Do you know any of those songs?" Rozia asked hopefully.

"No. I never did learn too much at school."

Rozia fell silent. He didn't even sound embarrassed by his admission.

The evening had turned to dusk. The robin that had a nest in the doorposts of Steve Nowak's abandoned store sat on a branch of a nearby tree and scolded them.

"Let's sit down on the steps and rest a minute," Casimir said, looking up and down the road. Except for Stanley and Beattie's figures disappearing into the evening light, the road was deserted. Everyone else had already gone home.

Rozia sat down by him on the old wooden steps, wishing that the walk was over.

Without warning, he grabbed her and bent her back on the porch. His big body pinned her down and his mouth, coarse and hard, was on hers so that she felt she would choke. In a surge of panic, she pushed against him.

"Quit wiggling," he snarled, and his hand fell on her leg.

"Beattie!" she screamed. "Beattie!"

"Shut up!" he said and clapped his hand over her mouth. She dug her nails into his hand and tried to kick him.

She heard running footsteps and Stanley's voice. "Casimir!"

Casimir let go of her and Rozia scrambled up from the porch, pulling her rumpled dress straight.

"Get the hell out of here," Stanley threatened. "What kind of person are you?"

Casimir didn't answer, but turned and walked off in the opposite direction.

"What's the matter with that dirty thing?" Rozia fumed, pulling once more at her dress. She felt as if she had smudges wherever Casimir had touched her.

"Are you all right?" Beattie asked.

Rozia's face flamed under their concern. "I'll be all right," Rozia said. "He's gone. I didn't mean to spoil your walk. Go on. I'll be along."

She followed her rescuers at a discreet distance the rest of the way home. Would Stanley tell everyone about Casimir? She thought back and could see nothing that she had done, but she felt as shamed as if Casimir's attack was her fault. How would anyone know what she had or hadn't done? She had seen and heard the big boys snigger and talk about girls before.

Tears of frustration and helplessness burned her eyes until she could hardly see the two lovers ahead of her. How wonderful this day had started, and how dismally it had ended. She thought of Joe. Joe would never have attempted what Casimir had done. Her own timidity had ruined the last day of her school career.

❧ ❧ ❧

In late August she and Tata were coming home from Bay City, their wagon loaded with boxes and barrels of what they couldn't grow themselves. As usual with such trips, they had groceries for half the neighborhood besides. Tata now depended on Rozia to help him with the list of supplies for the coming months. She was still running through their purchases in her head when Tata interrupted her thoughts. "School will be starting soon. I'd like you to finish and go on to high school in Auburn." She hadn't told Tata that Miss Lindsey had told her the same thing. She was already older than the others in her class because of the time she had missed.

"I can't go back to school," Rozia said.

"Stepmother's back home now. There's time for you to go."

Even though Stepmother was back from Traverse City, she didn't handle things well, and now there was another baby to care for. "I would be sitting with a bunch of kids half my size," she said. More to the point, she would have to board with someone during the week. Auburn was fifteen miles away.

The sky was turning very dark and the humidity was as thick as a quilt. Rozia fanned herself with her hat.

Tata was silent for awhile and then he said, "Looks like we'll have rain before we get home." Rozia had already felt the first drops on her sweaty face. She looked at Tata's profile in the approaching dusk. She knew he hadn't finished with the subject of school. "Giddup Dan," he said. The horse picked up his pace for a minute and then resumed his plod.

The night came quickly and then the rain started. They weren't more than half-way home, and Rozia couldn't even see Old Dan's rear in the darkness. The wind picked up and lightning flashed.

"Easy, Dan, easy," Tata said, but he might have been saying it to allay Rozia, who was clutching the edge of the buggy. When the horse suddenly stopped, Tata did not urge him on, and with the next flash of lightning, Rozia saw that the buggy's wheels teetered at the ditch's edge.

"Tata!" Rozia cried, terrified.

Dan veered back into the road.

"Old Dan will get us home," Tata said. "I just give him the reins. He'll get us there."

The trip seemed endless to Rozia, shivering in her rain-soaked dress, but Tata was right. Dan finally rolled the buggy into their driveway. Rozia jumped down, and the horse and buggy disappeared into the barn. Everyone in the house was already sleeping, but the kitchen was still hot and smelled like the cabbage and potatoes the family had for supper.

When Tata came in, Rozia was toweling her cream-colored straw hat, but she could see it was ruined. The small flowers had bled into the lighter color, and the perky brim had gone limp. But Rozia was glad to be home in one piece. "Dan saved us, didn't he Tata?"

"He's a good old horse."

Rozia continued to scrub at the hat, and Tata stood there. "What about school?" he finally asked.

"Tata, you said once that if I learned to read and write, I would never be ignorant. I could learn anything I wanted to. I know how to read and write."

Tata looked like he wanted to say more, but then he nodded and turned away. As it turned out, Tata's choice would have been the better one, but Rozia did not go to school again.

VIII

Evil eye and averted head...
fierceness of family and local feud.
Gaunt figures of fear and of friendliness...

~ John Montague

Rozia got to church early. Two years had passed since she left Cherry School. She was past fifteen now and walked the three miles to St. Valentine's church every Sunday that she got the chance. It was one of the times she got away from the overfull, over busy house that she struggled to maintain. In the last years Stepmother had two more babies, Verna and Helen, and her recovery after Traverse City had not been a complete one. She still did not do well with handling the growing family, and her resentment of Rozia continued to smolder, although with Tata home, most of the kicking and slapping had stopped. Tata was too busy and worried to say much, and it wasn't his way to talk much anyway, but sometimes he sent her out of the house just to get away. He would bring Stepmother and the others in the buggy.

This first Sunday of Lent was cloudy and cold and a northeast wind stung Rozia's face, a sure sign of more snow. No sign of spring yet. She found shelter in a corner by the church steps and waited for the priest to open the door.

At first, pioneers in the area traveled fifteen miles to St. Joseph's church in Auburn. Then in 1888 a Jesuit missionary, Father Szulak came to Beaver Township and offered mass once a month at John Nowak's house, the biggest house in the neighborhood. John was Anna

Trombley's dad, and several of Anna's ten brothers, who had once filled his house, still lived in the area. At the time, there were only 29 families in the budding Beaver Township parish, but the following year on St. Valentine's day, Jahn Zboraslski donated land for the church and a school.

Oddly enough, the school was built first and mass was held there until the church was built in 1909. By the time Rozia was growing up, a small settlement with a store and a blacksmith shop developed around Saint Valentine's. But the growing parish still depended on a missionary priest.

As Rozia felt warm relief from the wind, other women began to gather on the church steps. Even though she couldn't see them, Rozia knew they were bundled in heavy, dark coats. The cold Lenten season would not see spring-colored dress until Easter. In her hidden shelter, she could hear the ladies clearly, comparing this Lenten season's weather to last year's, and household details that Rozia often found useful. She had always relied on listening and watching when no one noticed she was around.

Suddenly she heard a voice stand out from the others. "Did you hear that one of Agnes Swiecicki's babies is not hers?"

Rozia almost leaned out of her hidden spot. Agnes. That was Stepmother's name.

"No! What do you mean?" a voice followed the shocked silence.

"Yes. Yes, she told her mother that the one is hers and the other is the girl's– Rozia's."

Rozia shrunk against the wall. They were talking about her.

"No!" another voice said, but it was not the voice of disbelief.

The first voice lowered but Rozia had no trouble hearing what she said. "And do you know what else?" The women on the church steps were totally quiet. "Rozia's baby is by her own father!"

Like a flock of chickens, they all started pecking at the new morsel. "Shocking!" "And he comes to church every Sunday, the hypocrite!" "Terrible!"

Rozia looked across the field where she had walked. Her first memory of home and church was that field, and for a minute, the memory blocked out the horrible chatter. When she was four, her cousins brought her to church on Christmas morning across that field. Her mother had gotten her up and they had said a prayer of thanksgiving in front of the first Christmas tree Rozia had ever seen in their parlor. Tiny sugar candies in the shapes of frying pans hung from the branches, and popcorn strings festooned the dark green. On the way to church, the moon was still shining and the snow glistened like angel hair and crackled with frost. Her cousins grabbed her, one on each side, and swung her over the sparkling field, their laughter floating through the magic morning. She had been so happy that morning.

She felt the cold wall against her back. How long ago that was. "Mama," she whispered. "Mama and Mother Mary, help me."

"What's the news, ladies?" a new voice broke into the women's chatter.

"Mrs. Gregorcyck, the most terrible thing"--

Rozia listened to the whole story again and she felt as ashamed as if she had done the horrendous deed they told. Her face felt as if it was burning and her head was light and dizzy. She thought that this might be how ladies fainted in the stories she had read, but she couldn't faint. She would fall where they could see her. Only ladies in stories could faint.

"Ladies! Ladies! What kind of talk is this?" Mrs. Gregorcyck's scolding voice cut through the women's expressions of outrage. "It's all nonsense! I know George Swiecicki. I know the family. That is not the truth."

The ladies in their great, dark coats fell silent. Mrs. Gregorcyck was well thought of. They would not disagree with her. "Agnes is a simple woman," Mrs. Gregorcyck said. "That story came from her own head."

The wooden door clicked and swung open, and Rozia watched from her corner as the ladies greeted the priest. "Good morning, Father." "A good day to be in church, Father." They filed in and soon the men who stood in the yard by the horses came up the steps stomping and blowing on their cold hands. She didn't even stir when Tata and the family came up the steps. Rozia waited until everyone had gone in before she crept alone to the back pew of the chilly church, vowing to remember Mrs. Gregorcyck in her prayers until the day she died.

Rozia didn't tell anyone the shameful story she had overheard, but now she knew that Stepmother's imaginings were worse than she had ever thought. She went home with the family and put the chicken dinner on the table. For most Catholics, Lent was a dour time when fasting meant that the other two meals of the day could not exceed the main meal, and most Lenten meals were meatless. For Rozia's family, it wasn't much more than their usual fare but on Sundays in Lent, the strict laws of fasting were lifted, and it was the family's one great meal of the week. Rozia could now fry chicken until it was crispy brown and mash potatoes until they were as light and fluffy as a summer cloud. Her baked beans were as good as any woman's in Beaver Township. Today she took no pride in the meal she had created, but if she was unusually quiet, it was hardly noticed in the big, noisy family.

In other years, Rozia had always loved the Lenten season. During the week, the neighborhood teens carried lanterns to church, and Mr. Brezinski led the Stations of the Cross. In spite of the solemn evenings, the frogs were singing, the pussy willows were budding, and the teen procession was alive with fun and a shared alliance as full of life as the spring around them. But this spring, after what Rozia had heard on the church steps, the Lenten season was heavy and dark. Every murmur she heard, every glance she saw must be about her.

Easter Sunday dawned warm and sunny enough for everyone to wear spring colors to Easter mass. Likewise, the church statues, covered during Lent with dark drapes now smiled on the parishioners, the priest was dressed in white, the altar was decorated with as many buds and greenery as the spring could produce, and the choir sang hymns of alleluia. St. Valentine's celebrated the Resurrection with all of the relief that spring brings after a long winter. For Rozia, Easter Mass was a warm respite. The music, the candles, the spring colors took her through the day of a ham dinner and even a cake that Stepmother had baked for the occasion.

But the next day, Rozia's cousins, the Nowak boys and Ted Ciacuch showed up early in the morning, their first stop on their neighborhood rounds. The Monday after Easter, the traditional day of boze rany (God's wounds), boys showed up at the door of a girl and she provided a treat or got the willow switches as retribution. Rozia hastily gave out Easter cinnamon buns before they could ever raise their willow switches, but she didn't share her neighbors' high spirits. The switches reminded her that perhaps the whole neighborhood thought she deserved the sting of retribution. She had done nothing evil, but she did not belong to the carefree, spring frolic of the young people in the neighborhood. She was gossiped about as if she was a woman– a bad woman. When Mr. Switala rang the evening angelus, as he had done three times a day ever since she could remember, Rozia only felt relief that the day was over.

IX

She went and stood
Under her father's vaunting oak
Who kept his peace in wind and sun...

~ JOHN CROWE RANSOM

Stepmother awakened right after Tata went out to feed the horses. The rest of the house still slept, but Rozia heard every sound the house made. She suppressed a groan when she heard the creak of the kitchen chair where Stepmother often sat, glued to that corner chair, staring into space as if she watched a parade of demons passing in front of her.

Rozia pulled on her work dress, a hideous gray thing that, nevertheless, could go days before it looked as soiled as it was. It looked as bad as the ones Mama had sewn. Mama might be an angel, but she was no seamstress. Rozia remembered a gray flannel one that Mama had made, a simple dress that Rozia had worn to school. It was not pretty at all. Now, Rozia had a few better dresses she wore to church that Anna Trombley had made. Rozia's favorite was one that her Aunt Berna had made one time when Tata had taken Rozia to Bay City. Her aunt was a seamstress and made wedding dresses and tailored suits. The dress, a red and black plaid wool, fit her perfectly and Rozia wore it every chance she got. But today was not a day to think about dresses.

Rozia slipped down the stairs and padded barefoot across the autumn-cold kitchen floor. She struck a match to the kindling, and soon the fire in the range was roaring. Then she pulled the big copper boiling kettle over the heat. She had filled it the night before and as soon as the water was hot, she would scrub the piles of laundry sorted in the pantry, starting with Tata's long underwear.

That bleak spring day when she had learned the awful rumor on the church steps seemed a lifetime ago, although it had only been a year and a half. Rozia had stayed in Bay City last winter and worked in Mercy Hospital's laundry room six days a week. Her brothers were older now, and Stepmother had less to cope with, but Tata still needed to be home, and the family needed the extra income. Laundry at Mercy Hospital was easy compared to washday at home with the scrub board and hand-operated wringer. She would have liked to stay there the whole year, but she was only there between crop farming, as so many of the girls were. Rozia wondered who did the laundry when they all had to come back home to help with the field work.

Louis Danielski, the first documented Pole in Bay County, arrived in 1870 and was responsible for sponsoring at least sixty-four other Polish families settling in and around Bay City, farming or working in wood mills and salt mines. By the early 1900's, Polish people were nearly 25% of the county's population and filled the south side of Bay City. Although the older people held strongly to the same traditions Rozia knew at home, her generation spoke the English they learned at school and easily found jobs in the growing city.

A smile tugged Rozia's straight little lips. She liked Bay City, and no one there knew the evil gossip about her. Perhaps that was why Tata had sent her away. Before she had come home for the summer, it turned hot and she and Louise Klinsky took walks at midnight to escape the stifling heat in their cupola room. Men would pass them on the street and tip their hats. "Good evening, ladies," they would say. She was only sixteen, but it was nice to be called a lady as if she was a heroine in a novel. And in the distance, someone sang:

K-K-K- Katie
My beautiful lady,
You're the only g-g-girl that I adore.
And when the m-moon shines
Over the cowshed
I'll be waiting at your k-k-k- kitchen door.

❧ ❧ ❧

Rozia had been good at her job at Mercy Hospital. Sister Fidelis and Sister Corona made a big fuss over how nicely she ironed their white habits. Sister Fidelis said she ought to be a nun. Rozia's smile widened. Her– a nun. What an idea! You had to be a saint to be a nun. She was nothing but a farm girl, but she was proud that she brought back some money to help out the family.

The back door slammed. Tata had fed the horses. He always fed the horses before he ate himself. Rozia quickly got the cast-iron fry pan down and took out side pork and potatoes from the pantry. The kids' oatmeal could wait. Tata needed a big breakfast to get started on the sugar beets today. Good fall weather never lasted long enough.

Tata walked in from the backroom and washed his hands and wiped them on the roller towel. He looked from Rozia to Stepmother sitting in her corner. He stalked over and stood over her, his dark eyes glinting. "Do you want to go to Traverse City again?" he said quietly.

Stepmother looked up at him, her eyes wide with her unnamed fears and shook her head violently.

"Then get up and set the table."

Like a frightened child, Stepmother ran to the cupboard and pulled out plates and bowls, not bothering to count them. Rozia stood at the stove and turned the spattering side pork as if she didn't see a thing.

The rest of the day, Rozia worked at the heavy wash. Stepmother lapsed into her state of frozen silence at her kitchen corner as soon as Tata left for the fields. She hardly moved until the late afternoon sun slanted through the window. Then she slipped into the pantry and brought out potatoes to peel.

Rozia hurried to get the wash tubs out of the kitchen before supper.

"Stop that banging," Stepmother said. It was the first thing she had said all day.

Rozia scooped a pail full of dirty water out of the tub. "I'm not banging," she said. On hindsight, she shouldn't have said anything, but she was hot and tired, and she truly was not banging anything. In spite of all she tried to do to help Stepmother, it was met with nothing but criticism.

Stepmother whirled and in one quick movement, hurled her paring knife at Rozia. The knife, catapulted with more anger than accuracy, somersaulted in the air and landed against Rozia's back, lodged in her apron straps.

In the same instant, Uncle Mike walked in the kitchen door. Short and stocky, he looked nothing like his tall, rangy stepbrother. He had come in from the field to tell his brother's wife that the day's work was done. Now his dark handsome eyes swept the scene from the older woman to Rozia, transfixed, pail in hand, the kitchen knife still lodged in the straps of her apron. His mouth tightened and he strode across the floor. "I think we've seen enough," he said shortly and took the knife and put it back on the cupboard.

Two days later Tata told Rozia, "You are going to Detroit to Clara's. I will take you to the train Saturday." That was all. It didn't occur to Rozia to question Tata's words. If he offered a suggestion,

Rozia was free to accept his words or not, but when he gave an order, it was to be obeyed. She knew that Uncle Mike had told Tata about Stepmother's badly-thrown knife and felt a mixture of humiliation and apprehension at being sent to Detroit. She didn't know cousin Clara well, and she had never been past Auburn or Bay City.

When she boarded the train Saturday morning, the passenger car smelled like leather from the worn black seats and like somebody's leftover lunch, a tantalizing aroma of fruit and fried chicken that made Rozia's stomach, already twisted in excitement, roll in hunger. The car was half-empty and Rozia found a seat by the window. She sat down and put the carpet bag down by her stiff Sunday shoes, trying to look like this wasn't the first time she had ever been on a train.

The train began to move and Rozia looked out of the window at the platform below. Her dad stood there, his eyes searching the car windows. "Tata," she said aloud and waved. frantically, but he couldn't find the window where she sat. She pressed her face close to the glass. "Tata!" she cried. The train's whistle wailed and she saw tears on her dad's farm-weathered cheeks before the train started moving and the station disappeared from view.

X

What shall I do now? What shall I do?
I shall rush out as I am, and walk the street
With my hair down, so.

~ T.S. Eliot

Detroit was huge and growing ever bigger. Dubbed the 'Paris of the West' in the gilded age, the city's wealthy had built homes that looked like palaces Since Henry Ford had opened the first auto factory in Highland Park in 1899, the city was humming with the new industry. Detroit had the first traffic light in the United States on Woodward and Grand Avenue, and in a few short years it would be known as the auto capital of the world. Detroit was hungry for workers like Rozia. They came from Michigan farms, and Detroit's factories swallowed them up. The places were dingy, the pay was poor, but to girls like Rozia, brought up on back-breaking labor under a hot sun, the chance for city life was irresistible. The wave of immigrants was a tsunami. A decade after Rozia lived in Detroit, the census numbered Polish population at 66,000.

Rozia boarded at Clara's, Uncle Mike Ciaciuch's oldest daughter. Clara's home was not one of the gilded mansions but a small, decent place on the east side of the city where German and Polish immigrants had settled. Soon Rozia got a job in the same factory as her cousin, Dora, although the two girls worked putting together overalls, not auto parts. After Aunt Antoinette's death, Dora, too, had acquired a stepmother, but her stepmother, Mary, was a gentle woman rescued from the financial straits of widowhood by Uncle Mike, and Dora had grown to be a bright and cheery girl. Rozia was

Rozia at Stephanoski's in Detroit

glad for her company.. Dora reminded Rozia of the good parts of home and family on the Beaver Township farm.

But less than three months after Rozia had arrived, Dora announced, "I got a better job than making overalls. I'm going to be a live-in housekeeper." She made a face and giggled, "And take care of kids."

Rozia was upset. "When did you decide that?" she cried. The thought of working in the big factory without her cousin was unthinkable. Detroit was too big and too full of noise and busy people that didn't work by the sun or the seasons but by the factory whistle and the clock, and the women she and Dora worked with talked about food and clothes and places that were as foreign to Rozia as if they came from another planet. Dora was her only compass in this foreign world she found herself in.

"I just found out today after church," Dora said. "Did you see that lady I was talking to?"

Rozia hadn't. Dora was always talking to people Roxia didn't know. "That was Mrs. Sosnowski. I told her I would let her know. I didn't want to seem too eager. But I've already made up my mind."

Rozia was silent. She wouldn't have thought to do that herself.

"It's better than the factory, Rozia. I know I can get you a job housekeeping too."

"I don't know, Dora," Rozia fretted. "I just don't know what to do."

As it turned out, it wasn't Dora who persuaded Rozia to leave her factory job. Amelia Klinsky had also turned up in Detroit from back home. Rozia remembered her as the flirtatious sister of Louise Klinsky, who had worked with Rozia in Bay City the winter before. Amelia's flirtations had finally brought her to grief. She was leaving the service of the Stephanowski's, a 'girl in trouble' and she recommended Rozia for her job.

When Mrs. Stephanowski showed up at Aunt Clara's door, Rozia didn't know if she wanted to do housework and take care of kids. She had been doing that all her life and living in a stranger's house didn't appeal to her at all. But Mrs. Stephanowski was persuasive and Rozia didn't know how to say she'd think about it as Dora had done. She accepted Mrs. Stephnowski's offer. She would have to find somewhere else to stay anyway. Clara had told her only days before that she had decided to move back to Bay City. Life in Detroit changed as rapidly as the city itself.

At first Rozia was intimidated by her new job with people who lived so differently than any she had ever known, but Rozia soon found her job on Field Street less fearsome than she expected. Although the two-story house and five children needed constant tending, Rozia found the care of a city home easy. Mister, as Rozia called Mr. Stephnowski, was a lawyer and real estate agent, but the Stephanowski's were not ostentatious. Their home was furnished for durability. A leather couch graced the parlor instead of velvet or brocade. "It's sturdy– for the children you know," Missus explained. The children were not indulged and pampered as Rozia had expected from stories she heard from other girls who held similar positions. Mr. and Mrs. Stephanowski both insisted on discipline. Although the children did not have fields and woods, they had a huge playroom in the basement, a luxury Rozia could never imagine in the houses she knew.

The basement housed not only the playroom, but a huge coal furnace. Although Mister cleaned the furnace and the coal bin on Saturdays, he often found that Rozia had already done the job. "Mrs. Sosnowski was right," Missus said to her husband. "Country girls aren't afraid to work. I'm so glad we found Rozia." Before long, they trusted her enough to leave the house and children in her care when they took business trips to Chicago or New York.

Mister's young secretary, Harold Mog, visited the house frequently when the Stephanowski's were out of town. Rozia knew that Mister had instructed the young man to check on her, but she enjoyed the attention nevertheless.

One weekend he showed up early. "Come on kids, we're going to Boblo Island."

"But Mr. Mog," Rozia protested, "that's a whole day for you."

He smiled at her. "And a nice whole day it will be," he said.

A band played on the ferry and the kids were beside themselves with giddiness at the dancing water and summer sunlight. Rozia couldn't blame them. She was thrilled with the music and color and the festive people that filled the day.

"It takes an hour to get to Bob Lo," Mr. Mog said, "But the trip is half the fun."

"This boat is so big," Rozia said. "I don't see how something this big can float."

"It is big," Mr. Mog aaid.. "It holds 2500 people There's a dance hall on the second floor and a beer hall on the third if you'd like to see it."

"Not the beer hall with the children," Rozia objected.

"You're absolutely right," Mr. Mog agreed.

On his next visit, Mr. Mog announced, "Tonight it's Hotel Pontchartrain for dinner."

Rozia stared at him, terrified. "I've never been to a place like *that*." Rozia had seen little of the Detroit that the affluent were familiar with, but she knew the Hotel Pontchartrain was one of those places.

Mr. Mog was not one to take Rozia's protests seriously. "Then it's about time you were," he said.

Rozia's impression of the 'fancy' place was dark wood and rich, red table coverings and lighted chandeliers. She was so anxious that she and the children make a good impression that the evening was a blur, and when it was over, she was almost relieved to escape into the summer evening outside the ornate doors.

"That was a wonderful thing to do for us," Rozia said to Mr. Mog, "but it's no place for a country girl."

Mr. Mog's laugh rang out in the summer air. "I love you, Rose," he said. "In a platonic way that is."

Rozia had to look up 'platonic' in Mr. Stephanowski's dictionary that night. Although Harold Mog was only in his mid-twenties, Rozia never called him by any other name than Mr. Mog. To be loved platonically was enough. It never occurred to Rozia to try and revise his platonic feelings toward her. Mr. Mog was not a man for a country girl either.

Mr. and Mrs. Stephanowski had tried once to introduce Rozia to a possible beau, but it did not go well. John Kruse was a country boy from Ohio, a son of some of Stephanowski's visiting friends. Rozia went to the movies with him, but poor John was as shy as Rozia, and they barely spoke to each other through the whole evening. Rozia was not ready for a romance in her life, even if other girls her age were already getting married.

When Mister and Missus returned from their trips, the children were full of stories of their adventures. They enjoyed their free time with Rozia, almost a vacation of their own. They ate dinner when they pleased and besides the trips with Mr. Mog, Rozia had taken them to Belle Isle. It was only a few blocks from Field Street, and the children enjoyed the pony rides, the swings, and the picnic lunch Rozia brought.

"You can go back," the oldest told his parents. "Rozia is so much fun."

Rozia experienced some of the great sites that historic Detroit's gilded age had to offer. Bob Lo Island, the English corruption of the

French name Bois Blanc, had originally been a fort island and was the headquarters of Tecumseh in the War of 1812. However in 1898, the 'Coney Island of Detroit' was born. Although it had carousels and other rides, it didn't have all that grew in the park's 100- year-old history, but it boasted Henry Ford's dance hall, the second largest in the world, that could hold 5,000 dancers at a time.

Belle Isle, another island in the Detroit River, opened its park in 1904, and was larger than Central Park in New York City. The conservatory, designed by Albert Kahn, who also designed the Cadillac Place and the River Rouge auto factory, held a botanical garden and greenhouse, and the Island also had a public aquarium, the longest continuous running aquarium in the United States until it closed in 2005.

Hotel Pontchartrain opened in 1907 and in Rozia's time the hotel, which held a thirty-two foot mahogany bar, was the meeting place for Detroit's industrial leaders. The current Hotel Pontchartrain is not the one that Rozia and Mr. Mog visited. That one was torn down in 1920. However, the modern one also sits on the site of the old French Fort Pontchartrain as did the original building designed by George Mason, who had also designed the Grand Hotel on Mackinaw Island.

Mister was so happy with the care Rozia had taken with his family, he beamed. "Rozia, you are so good to us, I'm going to do you a favor."

"Yes Sir?"

"You let me invest the extra money you make in property on Grosse Pointe. The money you put in now will grow and someday you will be a well-set young lady."

Rozia knew nothing about property, and it seemed a dreary place to put money she would rather spend at Kresge's, but Mister seemed so happy with the favor he was doing for her that she thanked him and the deal was done. With the remainder of her $9-per-week salary, Rozia began exploring Detroit on Sundays, her day off. One Sunday she found a neighborhood that resembled pictures of China that she remembered from her geography book; wooden pagoda roofs, banners on the shops with strange Chinese calligraphy, and men dressed in dark pajama-like pants with a single long braid in their hair.

Ahead of her, she saw people going into a building. It must be a coffee shop, Rozia thought, heady in the knowledge that she had enough money in her purse to stop and lunch like a city lady. She followed the others down a set of steps and through a heavy wooden door. It opened into a room, dark after the bright sunshine, and she stood inside trying to see in the dim light. The room, when she could make it out, was a huge hall, strangely bare except for red carpeting. Oriental men sat on the floor around strange objects from which several pipes extended on tubes. A few stared up at her with bemused expressions and the rest continued to pull on the pipes.

Rozia wandered about uncertainly, but no one came to assist her. Whatever this room was, they certainly were not going to serve coffee. She turned and walked back up the steps into the sunlight. She would call Dora tonight and they would have a good giggle about Rozia's venture into what she thought was a Chinese coffee shop, but when she rung up the Sasnowski's house, Dora had news of her own. "I'm leaving Detroit," she said.

"Dora! Why?" Rozia's voice ended in a plaintive cry. She had worked for Stephanowski's for a year now, and everyone she knew was going back home. In spite of her kind employers, Rozia counted on people from back home to be in the city too.

The Sasnowski parrot on the other side of the line squawked unsympathetically, "Dora! Dora! Dora!"

"Shut up your beak," Dora yelled.

"Dora, you can't," Rozia pleaded.

"I'm a little tired of this kind of work," Dora said. "I'm going to Bay City. Angeline's working in a restaurant there and they'll hire me because I'm her sister. I bet we could get you a job too."

The next day Rozia approached Mrs. Stephanowski with some trepidation and told her that she wanted to leave and go to Bay City with her cousin.

"Rozia! Why?" Mrs. Stephanowski cried in much the same way Rozia had cried the night before. "Haven't we been good to you? Aren't you happy here?"

"Everyone I know in Detroit is leaving," Rozia said.

Mrs. Stephanowski looked across the shiny dining-room table and, to Rozia's discomfiture, Mrs. Stephanowski's eyes filled with tears. "Rozia, I'm going to have a baby."

Rozia's eyes widened. Mrs. Stephanowski was not in the habit of sharing her personal affairs.

"You are so good with the children, Rozia, and they love you. I need somebody like you when my time comes. Do you understand?"

Rozia nodded miserably.

"Even if I found someone to replace you tomorrow, I don't know if I could trust her to do right. Please, Rozia," Mrs. Stephanowski pleaded,

Rosia couldn't say no. Dora left Detroit and Rozia stayed on.

Rozia and her cousin, Dora Ciaciuch

XI

Soul stretched tightly across the skies
That fade behind a city block...

~ T.S. Eliot

After Dora left Detroit, Rozia was lonely for people from home and went to visit Amelia Klinsky, although she and Amelia had never been close. When Amelia had left the Stephanowski's, as a 'girl in trouble', she had married a Russian Pole, who was not the father of her child, and she now lived in Hamtramck. Amelia's husband was a homely man, his face pocked from the dreaded smallpox. Rozia remembered her dad telling her that he had tied her hands when she had gotten the pox as a baby. "It was a cruel thing to do to a baby," Tata had said. "but you didn't get the scars." Now, looking at Amelia's man, Rozia was happy for Tata's foresight.

In spite of his homely face, or maybe because of it, Amelia's husband had adopted Amelia's baby girl wholeheartedly and treated the child better than Amelia did. And Mrs. Stephanowski had paid for her former hired girl's lying-in and bought clothes for the baby. "I have daughters," Missus had told Rozia, "Someday they may be in trouble and need someone to help them."

Amelia should have been happy that things had turned out as well as they had, but when Rozia arrived, she found Amelia in a pitiful state. "The man hasn't worked in months," she fumed to Rozia. "We've got to sell the kitchen range. Jesu!"

"It seems like he's trying," Rozia tried to comfort her.

"Trying! Trying! I don't care about his trying. He makes me sick."

Rozia went out and bought groceries which had to feed not only them, but two men boarders who had also lost their jobs. Rozia saw that city life hung precariously on whether someone was hiring or firing. On the farm, there might not have been a weekly paycheck, but there was always something to eat and wood for the stove.

As they washed the dishes after supper, Rozia tried to cheer up Amelia. "Remember when we went to that dance, Amelia?"

A small smile crept across Amelia's face. "I remember."

"And that man kept eyeing me up like he was going to ask me to dance."

Amelia's smile widened. "Is she married?" Amelia mimicked the words he had said to Rozia.

"It looks as though she's married," Rozia finished, and they both broke into laughter.

"It was that awful dress," Rozia said. "It fit me around the middle like I was five months pregnant. I never wore the thing again."

"He was a crude lout—but what can you expect of the Russian Poles?"

Rozia winced at Amelia's harshness. She didn't think Amelia's husband deserved such cruel words. Amelia went back to scrubbing a pan, her face grim. Rozia didn't mention that their dance night ended when Amelia had rushed up and grabbed Rozia by the arm. "Come on! We've got to run. Some guys are chasing me."

The evening was late by the time Amelia and Rozia had set the kitchen to rights and revived more of the Bay City stories like a couple of old ladies talking about their young days. When it was bed time, Amelia told her husband that Rozia needed to stay overnight and that he could sleep on the couch.

"No!" Rozia protested. "I can sleep on the couch."

"Nonsense," Amelia countered. "He can sleep on the couch. I don't want him in there anyway."

Rozia was taken aback at the bitterness in Amelia's voice and embarrassed at being the cause, but Amelia's husband said nothing. Perhaps the sleeping arrangement was nothing new.

The next morning when Rozia awoke, Amelia was already down in the kitchen fixing breakfast. Rozia heard a rustling on the other side of a screen that partitioned the bedroom and froze. The boarders and Amelia and her husband all slept in the same room! Why hadn't Amelia told her last night that she was sleeping in the same room with two strange men?

Rozia slid down farther under the sheets. They must have come in after she went to bed. She turned her back to the screen and pretended sleep, hoping they would leave soon. The door clicked and Rozia heard one set of footsteps down the stairway. She waited impatiently. Where was the other one? Had he left before she awakened?

Suddenly, the man came around the screen and with one step, slid into bed with her. His dark arms covered her bare shoulders.

She struggled up. "Amelia!" she cried. "Amelia!'

Amelia appeared at the door almost instantly, a spatula still in her hand.

"Get to hell out of there, you dirty thing!" she yelled brandishing the spatula like a sword.

The man obediently slid out of the bed and disappeared downstairs. Rozia jumped out of bed and threw her dress over the slip she had slept in. Amelia had already gone back to the kitchen.

The man was not at the breakfast table, and no one offered an explanation for his behavior. After a strained and hasty breakfast, Rozia left, although she had planned on staying at least half of Sunday. On the way back to Field Street from Hamtramck, she wondered what went on in that house, but she never went back there again.

After that, Rozia's only contact with home folks was Wladzia Jankowski, who had also married a Russian Pole and lived in Hamtramck. When Rozia visited, Wladzia's husband always walked her to the street car stop in the evening. "A young girl should not be on the street alone," he warned her. She didn't tell him that when she waited earlier, a carload of young men drove close to the curb and grabbed for her. She jumped back, but they got her new hat, a blue velvet cloche with two feathers arching over the top. She had deliberated at Kresge's for two weeks over that hat before she bought it. Detroit was losing its appeal.

The months went by. Mrs. Stephanowski delivered a baby boy, and Rozia took charge of him almost immediately. She knew a lot about babies from home. She wondered how her brothers and sisters were doing now. They were no longer babies; had Stepmother's resentment towards Rozia turned on another? Tata wrote seldom and always in Polish, lapsing into the language that came easiest, but the letters were not much more than brief notes in acknowledgment of the letters she wrote. It didn't matter. Rozia found that she liked to write just for the sake of writing, and she was proud that her penmanship was still as good as it was back in Miss Lindsey's classroom.

Eight months after the baby was born, Mister and Missus again entrusted Rozia with their family and left for a day to themselves. Rozia was startled when the doorbell rang. She was not expecting Mr. Mog, and the Stephanowski's did not have drop-in company. Rozia cautiously opened the door a crack and there stood Tata in his Sunday suit.

Rozia let out a small scream and flung the door wide open. "Tata! How did you get here?"

A small smile creased his weathered face. "By the train. I came to see how it is where you work."

He followed her into the front room. Rozia thought quickly.

Surely, Mister and Missus wouldn't mind if Tata sat in the front room and she offered him something to drink. They would surely do the same.

The children came in and stared curiously at the tall stranger, and he stared gravely back at them. "This is my father, children," Rozia said.

The children greeted him and the oldest asked him to please be seated. Tata sank gratefully into the leather chair, and Rozia nervously poured him a drink from a bottle of some sort. She only knew Tata to drink beer, but Tata took the glass she offered and sipped it carefully while she found herself rattling on about life on Field Street. The children sat as quietly as Tata through her recital. They had been taught early the value of being seen and not heard when there were guests in the house.

Tata finished the drink and stood up. "You are in a nice place," he said and moved towards the door.

"Tata! You're not leaving! Mister and Missus will be back soon. I'm sure they would want you to eat with them."

"I have to catch the next train," he said. "I wanted to see where you work. You are in a nice place. And these are nice children."

His visit lasted less than two hours, but after he left, Rozia felt more homesick than ever. Tata looked careworn. She needed to be closer to home.

That same week Rozia again stood across the shiny dining-room table to face both Mister and Missus, and again she announced her intention to move back to Bay City. This time the couple realized that Rozia would not be dissuaded.

"And Mister, remember the money you invested for me at Grosse Pointe?"

Mr. Stephanowski nodded. "It's already grown, Rozia."

"I'll need it when I go home."

Mister was more upset by this than he was with the prospect of disturbing their home with a new girl. "You can't do that, Rozia! This is long term, don't you see? It will accumulate and I will watch it for you as if you were my own daughter."

He tried to explain to her the intricacies of interest upon interest, but Rozia's only thought was that he had helped her save some money and spring was coming. Tata would need it for the spring planting. She wouldn't realize until years later how right Mister had been.

❧ ❧ ❧

When Rozia moved to Bay City, Aunt Bernice and Uncle Pete made room for her in their home and she got the restaurant job Dora had promised so long ago. In a few months, however, the family crush at Aunt Bernice's was too great and Rozia moved to Uncle Stan (Tata's brother) and Aunt Mary's to share a room with Dora.

Early mornings and long days didn't seem like a good reason to go to bed early when there were so many new things to share. Sometimes they paid ten cents for the movie on the corner and watched Pearl White, 'queen of the serials', in her continuing dramas on the flickering silent screen. They sat on their bed talking far into the night of "The Perils of Pauline" or the "Exploits of Elaine" until Uncle Stan would bang on the wall.

"Quiet down in there. A man's gotta get some sleep."

By Rozia's time, Bay City had greatly changed since the lumber era had put it on the map. At one time, fifty mills were active in the area, and an underlying salt basin further added to Bay City's rapid growth. Ship building was the newest industry in town. DeFoe's had gotten its first U.S. Navy contract in 1918, and continued as a major industry until 1975.

XII

Wholly to be a fool
while spring is in the world.

~ E.E. CUMMINGS

After Rozia moved to Bay City, she came back to the farm every weekend to help as best she could. Stepmother's hot resentment had abated, and Rozia was no longer the meek girl she had been only a few short years ago. The little extra money Rozia made that brought the family some relief may also have quieted Stepmother. The twins, Theresa and Tillie, had been born after Rozia left home, and Rozia suspected that Stepmother had already been pregnant that horrible day that had put Rozia on the train to Detroit. Little did Rozia know that one weekend the twins needed dresses for church would be the weekend that took her life in a new direction.

When Rozia walked in Anna Trombley's back door, Anna was chasing her son Vick and his Uncle Ted Nowak with a broom. "Them damn fools," she greeted Rozia. "I'm trying to work here and they walk all over my scrubbed floor with mud on their boots and then tangle my yarn on purpose! They're worse than kids."

Ted stood in the doorway, his eyes dancing. "Barwo Swienti," he started the mournful Polish dirge, but his lyrics continued with a twist. "Poor Jersey cow," he sang dolefully, "I'm coming for you."

Anna burst into laughter at his irreverence. "Get out of here," she said and shook the broom at him. He backed up and grabbed the milk pail and Vick followed him to the door.

Jerome Edward Trombley

"Do you want to go with me to Elmer Glancy's tomorrow?" Vick asked Rozia on his way out.

"Sure," Rozia said. She was surprised at the invitation, but she tried to sound as offhanded as he did.

Anna raised her eyebrows but said nothing as she and Rozia untangled the yarn and Anna took notes for the twins' dresses. Rozia noticed Anna's look. Did Anna think it was about time Vick started looking for something else besides an evening with his bachelor buddies? Or did she wonder that Rozia had captured his interest? Rozia had to wonder herself. Vick and his brother Ed had always been the big boys in the neighborhood, not a part of her girl-world at all. They both left school after their father died to help Anna with the farm, and that was back in Rozia's chart year. Ed, the older of the two brothers, took his position seriously as the man of Anna's house. Out of their mother's earshot, Vick called Ed 'Mr. Eddie' and teased him mercilessly. Once, in back of the barn, where Anna couldn't see, they took horsewhips after each other, while Anna's team, Prince and Bill, looked on nervously. Rozia and Walt could hear the cursing and the whips cracking from across the road where she was working.

Rozia had always liked Ed. When he helped with threshing and she and Walt had brought the shocks of grain to stack on the wagon, he would say, "Easy there, kids. You're working too hard." Rozia, ever susceptible to kindness, fell in love with him with all the intensity of a small girl for an older boy.

That was years before Rozia had left home. Then the country joined the First World War, a time that changed their world forever. When the war first started, Rozia remembered Tata and Uncle Mike arguing whether the United States should get involved in the European mess, although both agreed that Germany had to be the main culprit. After all, they both came from Poland that already had a long history with Germany.

The German and Polish neighbors in the township had gotten along well enough away from the political turmoil of the old country. They had come here to escape war. But war made men crazy. One of their German neighbors had been thrown out of Crump saloon, not because he had a German name, but because, after a few beers, the farmer found it necessary to defend his native country.

When Ed Trombley was drafted and sent to France, Rozia had already moved to Detroit. Vick had been deferred as a widow's only other son and sole support. Tata had given her that news in one of his infrequent letters when she was still at Stephanowski's. On a hot day in July, 1918 two young soldiers came to Anna Trombley's door to tell her that Ed had been killed in the trenches by 'friendly fire'. Tata told her that the whole neighborhood heard Anna's screams of grief. The war had hit home.

For the first time, Rozia understood that the bigger world sent its ripples into their lives, something she would see again and again. Already, the strange flying machines Tata had told her about years ago had been used in the war, and predictions were that someday they would all be able to fly from one side of the country to the other in a matter of hours. Rozia could believe it. Henry Ford's cars were not an unusual sight anymore. Now, three years after Ed's death, Vick was farming his mother's farm alone and he had his own Maxwell car.

Rozia was a little apprehensive about Vick's invitation. He was seven years older than she was and Vick and his Maxwell car was still part of the older boys' world. Vick and Elmer Glancy were first cousins and close friends. If either brought a woman into their bachelor times together, the other would pass judgment quickly.

Of course, Rozia reflected as she walked home, she was not a little girl anymore either. She had worked away from home for four years now. She almost laughed aloud when she thought that she had finally become the young lady Grandma Swiecicki had always told her she could be. She felt as young and lovely as the spring bursting in bloom around her.

Rozia and Vick Trombley

XIII

Spring is at work in woodlands bright with sun;...
Slip on this ring and this green gown, these laces;
The wood is furniture with resting-places.

~ John Ormand

After the evening with Vick at Elmer Glancy's and a few other young people of the neighborhood, Rozia went back to Bay City in an unsettled mood. They played cards, and Rozia did not know how to play cards. They sang Polish songs that Rozia didn't know. Would Vick ever ask her out again? Vick had given no hint and Rozia had so little experience with men that she had no idea what Vick's offhand invitation had meant. She worked the week waiting for the weekend when she would go home. She would see Vick again, even if she went over to Anna's on the pretext of an errand. If he ignored her, it was nothing but a hill of beans. She was doing okay all by herself.

The next weekend, it didn't take Rozia long to walk across the road to check on the progress of the twins' dresses. As she walked into Anna's yard, Vick met her before she even got to the door.

"Pick a flower for your hair," he said abruptly waving his hand at the multitude of flowers that filled Anna's yard.

Rozia hesitated.

Vick noticed her reluctance. "Ma works out here when she's done with the day. She does this for fun. Go ahead, pick a flower. She won't care."

Rozia stooped and picked a small yellow flower from a bush especially loaded with blossoms.

Vick looked at her choice and his heavy brows knit. He took it from her hand and threw it into the grass. "Not yellow," he said. He picked a pink rose and gave it to her. "This one is prettier."

"You don't like yellow?" Rozia said.

"No," he answered shortly. "You want to go to the show tonight?"

"Yes," she said.

She didn't know until much later that the roses on Ed's casket were yellow. Vick's feelings about his brother's death and his own deferment were painful feelings he had kept to himself. How had he and Anna felt that day in November of 1918 when the war was over? Church bells rang and factory whistles blew all over Detroit, and back home, the local boys shot their guns in the air. Tata didn't have any shells, so he touched off a stick of dynamite.

That night the moon came up late and high, full of summer promise. Rozia couldn't remember what movie they watched, but it certainly wasn't Pearl's dilemmas. When they drove into Tata's driveway, Rozia didn't want the time to end. She wanted to sit in the beautiful evening forever, the wilting rose still tucked in her hair.

"Remember when you played the harmonica for us at the hall, Vick?" she asked dreamily. The hall was on Lixey's Corner on the intersection of Beaver and Eight-mile Road, which also had the more unfortunate name, Tar Paper Corner.

He leaned back against the leather seat. "Yes. You were just a kid then."

The light was on in the house. Rozia could see her dad in the kitchen. He was usually in bed by this time.

Vick smiled. "We had some good times in that old building."

Tata's silhouette paced back and forth in front of the window.

"Old Ratajcyck wouldn't have had to let us play in there," Rozia said. "He did it just so we'd have some place to go."

Vick nodded, but Rozia wasn't really thinking of Mr. Ratajcyck's community generosity. She was staring at Tata's silhouette. Tata was watching her! The blood rushed to her head. Four years she had taken care of herself and here she was in Tata's own yard and he didn't trust her!

"If that isn't something!" she fumed.

"What?" Evidently, Vick hadn't noticed her dad's figure in the kitchen window.

"Tata– Look at him waiting for me to come in like a little kid."

Vick turned his head and watched the tall figure pace behind the curtains. "He's wondering what we're doing out here," he said.

"What does he think we're doing in his front yard?" Rozia sputtered.

Vick looked at her and she couldn't see his blue eyes in the shadowed car. He squeezed her hand and her fury subsided a little. She tried to explain how she felt. "One time when we were at the hall and Beattie and I were walking home, he was watching like that. I saw him on the road, but he went in the house before I got to the driveway."

Vick said nothing.

"I didn't like it then, and I was a kid. I'm not a kid anymore."

"No, you're not," Vick said and Rozia's face flamed and her heart fluttered the way he said that. For a minute, she forgot the pacing figure in the kitchen window.

Vick leaned closer and smiled. "Where did you get those pretty brown eyes that are always looking around?"

"I-I don't know." Rozia felt flustered and confused by this new turn in their talk. She opened the car door. "I guess I'd better go," she said.

Vick nodded and started the car. "See you in church," he said. She learned in time, it was his signature farewell and had nothing to do with church.

Tata said nothing to her when she went in, and Rozia said nothing to him. But a small flame of rebellion was lit. She was going to live life her own way. Her heart beat faster and her face flushed hot when she wondered what life would be with a man like Vick.

As the summer went on, Rozia looked forward to her weekends home, as she once looked forward to coming back to Bay City on Mondays. She now had her own apartment over Mrs. Morgenson's Restaurant (Uncle Stan was relieved), and she liked a place of her own, although sometimes the piano downstairs in the restaurant was a little noisy, especially if it was taken over by someone who didn't play well.

Her new living arrangement was all thanks to Bertha Laur. Alan Metiva had fallen in love with Bertha and won her over, but then Bertha found out that he was a married man with five children. As Rozia heard the story, Bertha insisted that he leave her alone, and lovestruck Alan fell sick and took to his bed moaning, "Bertha! My Bertha!" Bertha had no idea what Alan's wife thought of her husband's behavior, but Bertha was horrified at her unintended complicity in leading a married man astray. She left her apartment in haste and even sold Rozia the table and wardrobe that Alan had made for her.

Although Rozia didn't spend every weekend with Vick, he continued to ask her out, and she was happy for the attention. He was a different man than Alan Metiva or Mr. Mog or even Mosecelo, the Detroit streetcar Romeo, who had hinted he would like to see her when he wasn't piloting a streetcar. Vick was Anna Trombley's son, a man who would never fall into his bed and moan or write letters that declared she was breaking his heart, or tell her that he loved her in a Platonic way. He was a neighbor who had his life invested in a life she knew; saving the farm, working the fields. After Rozia's other brushes with men, Vick was a comfortable neighbor who didn't press her with unwanted advances.

Their dates were predictable. Evidently, Elmer Glancy approved of her because she was included in his evenings of card playing and impromptu music, and during the summer, there were local ball games. Vick played and Rozia cheered with the other neighbors, wives and girlfriends that gathered on a Sunday afternoon. Vick was short, barely two inches taller than she was, but he was strong and fast, and her heart leapt when his blue eyes flashed her way after he made a run or a good catch. She found herself looking forward to their good-night kisses, and she had no doubt that Vick did too. She knew nothing about what exactly happened after the kisses, but from the strange and wonderful stirrings she felt with Vick's kisses, she was beginning to understand how Amelia got herself in trouble.

Rozia's wedding: Groomsman, Theodore Nowak,
Maid of Honor, Dora Ciaciuch

XIV

I remember on that day
I was thinking only of my love...
But now I remember the day
as I remember my grandmother.

~ Dorothy Livesay

In the summer of 1922, after only three months, Vick said they should be married if she felt the same way. After all, they had known each other all their lives. His proposal was almost as offhand as his first invitation to Elmer Glancy's, but Rozia already knew that was the way Vick talked. She imagined Tata's proposal to her mother had been much the same way. A man's word was his commitment and elaborate flourishes were considered unnecessary, although their kiss that night was longer than ever before.

Rozia walked from Bay City to Kawkawlin to tell Busia Swiecicki, who was now in her 90's. In the years since her mother's death, Rozia had grown to appreciate the woman who had taken care of her and her brothers years ago. In spite of her brusque ways, her grandmother's instructions about how to be a young lady had come back to Rozia over the years. She kept her long auburn-brown hair neat and brushed. She didn't shorten her skirts the way many of the girls in the city were doing, and she kept herself and her apartment neat and clean. And Busia didn't need to tell her how to behave with Vick. She had always, in spite of her fluttering heart, behaved like the lady Busia had told her to be.

Since moving back to Bay City, Rozia visited Busia often, even though the walk was long. Once a man had given Rozia a ride and she was grateful, though he drove so fast it was a little scary. She had grown accustomed to cars, but why did they keep trying to make them go faster? She thanked the man when they got to Aunt Mary's driveway, but she went into the house glad the ride was over.

But today, after the long hot walk to Aunt Mary Martinski's, (Aunt Mary was Tata's sister), Rozia found that the indomitable old lady had sunk into a coma.

"Go talk to her, Rozia," Aunt Mary said. "We talk to her all the time. Who knows? She might hear us."

Rozia went into the bedroom and took her grandmother's worn, withered hand. "Busia, I hope you can hear me," she said. "Vick Trombley and I are getting married." The hand lay limp in her grasp. "We're getting married in September, Busia , the same month Tata married my mother. You've got to come to my wedding."

Busia lay as still as death, and tears stung Rozia's eyes. Every time she had visited Busia in the last years, Busia had asked when Rozia would marry. Rozia smiled at the shriveled figure through her tears. If Busia could hear, she would approve. It was what young ladies were supposed to do.

When Rozia patted Busia's hand and left, she knew her grandmother wouldn't be coming to her wedding. Busia died two weeks later. Rozia wanted to postpone the wedding. It seemed too close to the funeral of the family matriarch.

"Nonsense," Aunt Mary said. "She was waiting for this wedding. She'll know."

After Busia's funeral, Rozia studied her parents' wedding photo. How young Mama was, only sixteen. Even Tata, who was 27 back then, looked young and scared, much younger than his wedding picture with stepmother only nine years later. It could have been the moustache he had grown, but more likely nine years of caring for a farm and a family and burying his young wife had left their mark. How would it be for her and Vick in nine years? She quickly put the photos away. It was silly to have such thoughts. Busia's funeral must have dampened her spirits. Aunt Mary was right. The wedding would go on as planned.

Vick and Rozia were married September 11th, 1922. It rained and the wind blew so hard it seemed as if it would blow St. Valentine's church out of Beaver. Father Kwasigroh celebrated the wedding mass in his usual dour manner and Rozia wished St. Valentine's had a sunnier priest. Even his name meant sour peas in Polish. But the altar was decorated with what must have been half of Anna Trombley's flower gardens. Rozia and Vick walked up the aisle together halfway through the mass and when Ted Nowak, Vick's best man, produced the gold band that Vick slipped on her trembling finger, Rozia looked at it and then at Vick. He was smiling as if he had just given her the world, and she felt that he had.

Vick's sister, Gert, insisted that they drive to Bay City to have wedding pictures taken. The weather had abated somewhat, and Gert's dapper husband, Floyd, drove with the top down the fifteen miles to the studio, and the wedding party arrived in wild disarray. Rozia's bouquet of rosettes and white ribbons that she had gotten from a Bay City florist was in tangles when the studio picture was taken. Rozia thought of the last special day she had been in a photographer's studio with Aunt Antoinette for her First Communion. What a long time ago that was. She looked at Dora, her maid of honor, and wondered if she was thinking the same thing.

When they got back to Tata's, the wedding supper filled the table and Rozia noted that the kitchen looked clean and the parlor was dusted. Stepmother had worked to make Rozia's wedding a nice one. Rozia was sure that Anna Trombley had inspected and perhaps helped with putting the house in order, although Stepmother had improved since those first years. She and Tata had given them a feather tick for a wedding present. Rozia felt sorry that Stepmother's bad feelings for her had not disappeared until Rozia left home. So many years, so many bad feelings.

Of course Anna Trombley, who cooked for weddings all over the neighborhood, had donated heavily to the feast. Rozia smiled at her small, energetic mother-in-law with the bright, blue eyes that Vick had inherited. It seemed that Anna approved of her. Tata had told Rozia that he had gone to Anna's a few days before the wedding, and Anna was patting butter and waltzing around her kitchen. "I'm so happy Vick's getting married," she said, "and I'm glad it's Rozia and not that Amelia Klinsky Vick was after for awhile. She kept writing him even after she moved to Detroit." She winked at Tata. "I took care of that. I saw the letters first."

Tata had shaken his head at Anna's way of steering her son's affairs, but he had to smile. He liked Anna. She had done a good job with keeping her farm, not an easy thing for a widow to do, and Vick had been a helpful son. Rozia had chosen well.

After the wedding supper at Tata's, the wedding party moved to Anna Trombley's parlor. She had rolled back the rug to dance on her hardwood floor until the early hours of the morning. Although the wedding only included family, there was a lot of family and not many were inclined to miss the chance for a good party. The house was filled to overflowing. Rozia put her bouquet on the dining-room table, and as the night went on, each guest took a flower until the bouquet was gone.

As the wedding guests slipped away one by one, Rozia, still in her gown and veil, looked about for her new husband. He lay on the couch, and she slipped across the empty room to him. She stopped at the look in his eyes. I'm scared, she thought, this is my wedding night and now I'm scared. I wish everyone was still here and we were still dancing. She thought of Casimir on the wooden porch. She thought of Amelia Klinsky's boarder. She thought of the time she and Vick had gone to a picnic in Fisherville when he and Jiggy Piowak had left her on the dance floor and went downstairs to have a beer. A man who asked her to dance had held her so close, she pushed him away and ran from the room. Her encounters with men and sex had never been anything but scary, and now she was to lay with this man, and she had no idea what to expect except that babies were the result.

She looked around. Dora had left. Beattie was gone and so was Gert. Only Ted, Vick's best man, was left, rolling the rug back on the parlor floor. Vick's best man was the youngest of Anna's brothers, actually Vick's uncle but only a year older than Vick himself and another one of Vick's favorite bachelor buddies.

Ted was a fun-loving, irreverent character, but now he saw her consternation. "Who will take the bride's veil off?" he said. "They've all gone and there's only the poor best man." He walked over and carefully unpinned the crown from Rozia's red-brown hair.

That night Rozia slept in her slip. Her new sister-in-law, Gert, had sewn the hem of her nightgown together. Rozia and Vick spent their wedding night in Anna's house. It was to be Rozia's home for the next eleven years.

Anna Trombley and children, Ed, Gertrude,
Beatrice (seated) and Victor.

XV

Since then—'tis centuries—and
Feels shorther than the day...

~ Emily Dickinson

Anna Trombley was somebody to be reckoned with, and Rozia soon learned that living in her mother-in-law's house and dealing with Vick's family that she thought she knew was not what she had expected. Now that Vick was married, Anna felt free to spend extensive time with each of her grown children and she left the newly-married couple and went to Beattie's who had married; her first baby, Evelyn, was already a month old. Her other babies, Gene and Laura, were born after Rozia and Vick had started a family of their own.

Beattie's husband, Leo Reinhardt, was a short, stocky man that Beattie affectionately called her Dutchman, but Rozia soon wondered how her sweet likable sister-in-law had chosen such a man. Vick told Rozia one time when they were butchering pigs, Leo bragged he could handle half a pig by himself and fell down the basement steps with the pig on top of him. Even Vick, accustomed to all sorts of characters in his circle of relatives, didn't care for his bragging brother-in-law and his crude practical jokes and warned him away when Rozia was pregnant.

Gert and her husband, Floyd Kingsland, lived in Flint. Both worked at Flint Buick and made money as easily as they spent it. Gertie eventually had two sons, Don and Floyd, junior, although everyone just called him Junior. Gert was as lively as Beattie was quiet. She took up smoking and told jokes she heard at the factory that Rozia didn't always catch, but the men always did. Rozia felt a little timid around her flamboyant, good-natured sister-in-law, but Vick clearly loved Gert and her irreverent ways, and Anna joined in her daughter's jokes and songs. She had been the life of the party herself when she was young, which was probably what had attracted the party-loving John Holka to her, someone Anna would like to forget.

Anna's family had come from Gniezno, Poland to America through Boston in 1881. Anna was eleven years old and the only girl in a family of eleven. One sister died young. Although their surname in Poland was Nadskakula, Anna's father, John, shortened it to Nowak (which translates to 'new') when they came to America.

As soon as Anna could work out, she worked at a boarding house in Bay City to bring some income to the family, and that's where she met Adolph Douglas Trombley. When she married in 1891, she and her Doug, as he was called, moved to Beaver Township. At first they lived in a log cabin. The tiny and vigorous Anna surrounded the cabin with flowers and scrubbed it spotless, but snow sifted in on the boy's quilts up in the loft.

In those days when marriages were often a matter of convenience, Anna had married a man she really loved. Doug read to her, teased her, and carried her across mud puddles. She had only had one year of school after she came to America, but with Doug, she learned to read English. When he was reading *East Lynne* to her, she couldn't wait for him to read the next chapter. She picked up the book and stumbled through the half-familiar words herself.

Unlike Anna, Doug Trombley's family had been long-time residents of Bay County. Joseph and Medor moved into the region for its lucrative trapping and trading with Native Americans and in1837 built the first wooden frame house in Bay City on Water and 24th Street. Doug's parents, Adolphus and Harriet, had four sons and two daugh-

ters. Either Doug's mother or his grandmother was Native American. Doug's grandfather, Peter Trombley, had come to the United States by way of Canada and originally lived in Wayne County. He traded land on Grosse Point for a buggy and a team of horses to get to Bay City where he already had family.

When Doug died suddenly at 35, leaving Anna with four children, she was in a precarious situation. Kazmarek, a short square-built man, who spread gossip and innuendos like a church porch woman, told many neighbors, and often, that the Jankowski boy, at least ten years younger than Anna, spent too much time in her kitchen and who knew where else in her house. Soon enough, the gossip reached Anna and she seethed with anger. She depended on her good reputation in the small community and his story was untrue.

One threshing day at Tata's, Anna was setting up tables under the trees with the other neighbor women, when suddenly she left them. She picked up a two-by-four and marched to the field where the threshing machine sat and churned the stalks through its bowels and coughed grain into the hopper. When she reached the men, she advanced on the surprised Kazmarek. "Talk about me, will you?" she spit at him. She swung her weapon. He ducked and ran around the threshing machine. She chased him, yelling, "You and your dirty mouth!"

The other men laughed at the red-faced farmer chased by a disgusted widow and they put in their catcalls. "Faster, Kazmarek!" they called, "or she'll put you in the machine!"

Her marriage to John Holka a couple of years later brought no financial security. Even though Anna had caught John's eye at a neighborhood party, she was much more than a merry widow and unfortunately, John was not much more than a merry widower. After they married, he brought his children to Anna and left for long periods of time, supposedly working in Detroit. If he worked during his absences, Anna never saw enough money to support four extra children. It seems the only contribution he made to the family was introducing Vick to chewing tobacco.

After Anna showed John her well-scrubbed door, the two eldest Holka children, Bill and Frances, went to live with their other grandma, and baby Tom, a sickly baby, died shortly after. Only Alice Holka stayed with Anna until she was old enough to work on her own and came back to visit Anna even after she married. Alice liked her blunt stepmother.

Although Anna and John never lived together after Anna told him to go and live somewhere else, they never divorced. But Anna was through with men. She and her boys farmed and lumbered to make ends meet. She took in sewing and cooked for weddings, although she never followed a recipe. She learned by adding a dash of this and a pinch of that. She never rested.

But Anna never forgot. Years later, when John Holka ended up in a nursing home with his legs amputated and close to death, John's son, Bill, asked if she would visit his father. John wanted to set things right before he died. Anna declined. "Tell him I forgive him, but I don't want to see him," she told Bill.

Anna was as different from Rozia's stepmother as night and day. She was resourceful and knew how to do many things well, but she was also blunt and wanted things done her way. Even though Anna divided her time with each of her grown children, when she came back to her house, no longer a log cabin, but a two-story frame house, she inspected it like a little Polish general.

As time went on and Anna's extended times with Beattie and Gert revolved back to Anna's time with Vick and Rozia, Rozia's stomach always knotted. The old adage about two women in the same kitchen was especially true with Anna. "If the shade is up, she pulls it down. If it's down, she pulls it up," Rozia complained to Vick. "She can see dust under the beds when she's still in the kitchen."

Vick shrugged. What Rozia and his mother did in the house was women's stuff, and no man in their neighborhood who had a woman in the house knew one end of a dust mop from the other and most had never touched a cooking pot in their lives. Anna had raised her son to expect meals on time, a clean house and well-behaved babies. Gert and Beattie told Rozia that when they lived at home and the boys came in dropping mud on the floor, they cleaned it up and kept quiet. The men had hard work to do. What Rozia had seen the day Anna took the broom after Vick and his uncle was nothing but teasing. Anna cleaned up after a man and both Vick and Anna expected that Rozia would do the same. Rozia expected something different. Tata would never track mud across a kitchen floor.

XVI

When they were wild
When they were not yet human
When they could have been anything,
I was on the other side ready with milk to lure them...

~ Louise Erdrich

When Rozia found she was pregnant a short time after her wedding night, she was thrilled. Sex held little charm for her, but she wanted babies. It was the most important reason to marry. It hadn't occurred to her that Vick would think otherwise. "I thought we would have more time alone before we had kids," Vick said.

"If it was up to a man to have kids, the human race would have died out a long time ago," Gert laughed when Rozia told her sister-in-law what Vick had said. "Come and spend a few days in town before you have that baby. It's easier to carry them around when they're still inside."

They went to see the first talkie film Rozia had ever seen, "Man in the Moon".

"Talking pictures!" Rozia exclaimed. "What will they think of next?"

"Probably color," Gert said. "Now we've got to get your hair style up to the times."

"Oh Gert, I don't think so." Rozia was already well along in her pregnancy. A hair style up to the times seemed frivolous.

"I've already made an appointment. You'll love it, and it will be so much easier to take care of when the baby comes."

Rozia thought she looked rather stylish, but when she went back home, Vick did not like her new look at all, and of course Rozia had no way to keep the hair style anyway, so she let her hair grow out and never cut it again until she was well into her seventies.

Rozia planned on having her baby at home. Anna had midwived several babies in the neighborhood and had already helped bring her other grandchildren into the world. Women in bigger cities were now going to hospitals and being delivered by doctors, but having a baby was not an illness, and Rozia cringed at the thought of a strange man presiding over her baby's birth.

When Rozia's labor began on a hot day in July, Anna and Gert were already on hand. Anna had an uncanny knack for guessing the day of a birth, probably the accumulated observations of dozens of other pregnancies. But before long, Anna saw that this, the first of her son's children, was in trouble, and she knew her limits as a midwife. "Go over to Levessuer's. Call the doctor," she ordered Vick. Levessuer was the only one in the neighborhood who had a phone.

When Doctor Drummond came from Bay City, Anna sized him up; young, nervous– she had probably delivered more babies than he ever had. Jesu, why couldn't they have sent someone like a Doctor Herrick!

After a brief exam, he said, "She has to go to the hospital."

"No" groaned Rozia through her pain. The thought of going all the way to Bay City was more than she could bear.

"The baby can't be born without help," he said to Rozia. "You are in danger. The baby's in danger."

Anna and Gert were silent. What if the young doctor was right?

"Can someone drive her?" the doctor asked.

They looked at Vick. He had fainted across Rozia's bed the first time Anna had asked for his help. Now he sagged in a chair, his face ashen.

"My car only has room for one other," the doctor said. "What will we do?"

"Jesus, Mary, and Joseph!" Gert exclaimed. "I'll hold her on my lap. Let's go!"

On the way to Bay City, a train crept across the Linwood crossing. "Hurry!" the doctor said aloud, "Oh Lord, hurry!"

Rozia stiffened with pain. She had known little about sex when she married and she knew little about labor and birth. Neither her stepmother nor her mother-in-law talked of such things, but this pain was more than she could stand. Often babies died and sometimes mothers died too.

Gert shot the doctor a look of disgust. This man certainly did not inspire confidence.

When they got to the hospital and Rozia was put on a gurney and rushed to the delivery room, Rozia felt that she had left her pain-racked body. She saw herself on the cart from far above and watched as the white-coated attendants turned down one hall and then another until the delivery room door swung open. I wonder what will happen next, she thought and her thought was as if she was watching someone else.

The next thing she knew, Gert was leaning over her bed and slapping her hands. "Where are you Rozia? Where are you?" Her voice seemed to come from a great distance.

"In the hospital," she murmured. "I saw it all, Gert. I was a long ways away, but I saw it all. The doctor had to use forceps."

Gert turned to Vick and Rozia hazily wondered how he got there. "She'll be all right," Gert said. "It's all that morphine they had to give her."

"The baby. It's a boy," Rozia went on. "Where is my baby?"

"He's fine," Gert said. "Rest now."

After she recovered, Rozia knew it was not morphine that had taken her out of herself. She hadn't even had any morphine when she had left her body that afternoon, but she had no explanation for her strange experience, and so she dismissed it. Her baby was alive and she was alive. She was now a mother.

They named their first born Jerome Edward after Vick's soldier brother, but in the tradition of Vick's family, they all went by their middle names. Vick's dad, Adolph, had always been Doug (and this was before Hitler made Adolph a loathed name), Vick's brother had always gone by Ed and Vick's legal name was Frank Victor. Rozia never knew why. It just was, so her baby was Eddie until he was old enough to drop the diminutive.

Vick's Uncle Gus's wife, Mary, made the new arrival a beautiful Baptismal dress. Rozia was grateful, but Vick wasn't. Rozia was finding out that Anna's large family did not always set well with Vick. Although he liked his Uncle Theodore and his cousin Elmer Glancy, he resented Uncle Gus and Mary. Every Sunday they came to eat Anna's chicken dinners. "No chicken every Sunday with us," Vick reminded Rozia brusquely when they were newly-married and Anna had gone to stay with Beattie. Mary's gift did little to allay Vick's feelings. Rozia guessed that when Vick struggled to keep the farm together, his uncle's visits took from them thoughtlessly. Rozia also knew by now that Vick would never say as much. He was a man of few words and his words were the how and when, not the why.

XVII

"You all die at fifteen," said Diderot,
and turn part legend, part convention.
Still, eyes inaccurately dream
behind closed windows blankening with steam.

~ Adrienne Rich

Roseanne was born nineteen months after Ed. A year after that Lillian came, the baby that cried herself to sleep while Rozia worked in the field. Rozia had to run ahead of the team to get the bread baked and the baby changed before the next load of hay. Her heart turned over when she saw that Lillian often had tear streaks on her flushed cheeks and cuddled to feathers she pulled from the pillow. Elmer was born in 1927.

Rozia had expected to have a family and she wanted to love her babies, but her life had become so different than the mother she wanted to be. She didn't have enough time to do more than feed her babies, change them and keep them clean. She never had enough milk to breast feed past the first few weeks, and she didn't even have much time to cradle them in her arms and enjoy their baby warmth.

She had to rely on Anna a lot in those years. Although Stepmother had softened towards Rozia, she could not help. She was still having babies of her own. Rozia was godmother to Eleanor, who died in infancy. Clara, Leo, and Albert were born the same years as Rozia's own Lillian and Elmer. Rozia's understanding of her stepmother's desperation grew with her own burgeoning family.

In the years after Rozia married, her brothers had grown up right behind her. Walt married in a big Polish wedding in Bay City.

It was not a cause for celebration as far as Rozia could see, and she felt responsible for her brother's choice. He met his Louise at a birthday party Rozia had for Vick. As with most parties, everyone wanted to join in the fun. Louise's sister wrote and told Rozia to have lots of cream, and Rozia knew what that meant. They would be bringing beer, and everybody knew that cream before drinking was the antidote, but Rose was happy that her party would be a big one for Vick. But that day Walt met Louise and it was love at first sight for her sweet, gullible brother and his distant cousin, who quickly wrapped him around her little finger.

"She can't have children," Walt had confided to Rozia before the wedding.

"Think what you're doing, Walt," Rozia pleaded. "You are marrying without ever being able to have a family." It was so different, her worrying about too many pregnancies and wondering how her brother could get into a marriage, knowing that there would never be any children at all.

"I don't care, Rozia," Walt said. "I love her."

Rozia couldn't see his infatuation with Louise. When Louise visited, she wouldn't use the outside toilet, didn't want to leave the car because of her fear of chicken feathers. But she could certainly dress. Jewelry dripped from her and her dresses were always in the latest style. Even more, Rozia didn't like the way Louise later singled out her sister, Blanche's son, Ronnie, and pampered him to the exclusion of Blanche's daughter. As time went on, Louise even bought the boy a car. It didn't seem right to Rozia, but Walt was not the axe-wielding character with Louise that he had been when he was a kid and had almost chopped off Rozia's toe.

Rozia's brother, Vic, also married. His young wife developed peritonitis after she delivered their first baby. Vic held her hand and listened to her plan their life together in the hours before she died. It was the horrible end that had frightened Rozia when Doctor Drummond rushed her to the hospital while she was in labor with Ed.

Vic's in-laws, in hysterical grief, blamed Vic and took his baby girl, Lorraine. After that, his bouts of drunkenness and a perforated ulcer almost killed him. Rozia took her brother in and nursed him until he got better, but she got tired of his constant demands. He took more time and patience than the kids. Although his second wife was a good woman, his second marriage was still marred with his drinking.

As she churned butter the day after her brother, Vic, left, she reflected that marriage had not been good for any of them. Her own marriage had none of the drama of her brothers, but it was more frustrating as the years went on. When she lived at home, the whole business of running the house and the farm rested on Tata. Vick had lived with his mother ever since his dad died, and Anna was still clearly in command. Although she left for long stretches to stay with Beattie or Gert, when she came back, it was to her house. Vick never made any other decisions than when to cut the hay or hoe the beans. He left the hand that rocked the cradle to also lift the strap of discipline. When he needed help in the field, he expected Rozia to be out there. At home, Tata ran the farm, and Rozia wanted Vick to be like Tata.

XVIII

All others talked as if
Talk were a dance.
Clodhopper, I, with clumsy feet...

~ Denise Levertov

The days and months were an unending struggle to keep up with an ever-longer list of chores. Rozia seemed to fall further and further behind. Anna had grown beautiful flowers to relax after a day's work. Rozia could hardly wait to get the supper dishes done and put the kids to bed at the end of the day.

The routine of farm work was broken one night in 1927 when John Nowak, Anna's brother, had a party for all the neighbors. Parties were scarce, and Vick and Rozia went. It was prohibition days, so the beer was homemade and flowed freely, although Rozia had no idea where it had come from.

Prohibition and the years of the flapper were in full swing during Rozia's first years of marriage. John Nowak's party may have been a little nod toward the general resistance to Prohibition, but it also may have been a happy celebration at the good prices the farmers were getting for their cash crops. Beaver Township had no speakeasys and no investments in the ballooning stock market, and the farm women did not know how to do the Charleston, but perhaps their daughters who went to work in the city did.

Vick and Lena Karbowski, Uncle Frank and Aunt Tillie Nowak's oldest daughter, stood on the other side of the room cracking jokes and doing their imitations of neighbors who weren't there. Vick had a streak of irreverence quite like his sister, Gert, and the

(Frank) Victor Trombley

homemade brew brought it out in him. Rozia had to admire his talent for mimicry, even though she objected to some of his jokes. He had christened a three-legged cat who stumped up their wooden sidewalk at home 'ol Lixey' for the crippled saloon keeper at Beaver Corners. It seemed cruel to Rozia, but to Vick, it was just funny.

He and Lena had quite a group around them. Rozia suddenly felt apart from them all. Vick's family was so different from her own. She was no Anna and she was no Gert, and she didn't even joke around with Vick like his cousin Lena could do. She sat with her stepmother along the wall of the big kitchen, one ear listening for the kids put down for the night in the next room. She felt like a piece of furniture, a matron past dancing and never able to flirt and joke like the others.

Suddenly, Stepmother turned toward her and put a hand on Rozia's arm. "I want to say something, Rozia. All those years when you were home and I was so mean to you, I'm sorry. Will you forgive me?"

Rozia wondered if it was the home brew that had prompted Stepmother's unexpected apology. Those days had happened so long ago when her stepmother had stepped into a marriage and motherhood she couldn't realize, no more than Rozia had known. "Of course I forgive you," Rozia said.

They watched the party for a minute and then Rozia asked, "Remember the time when you went to see your mother and I tipped over the cake that you baked for Tata?" The one time in all of Stepmother's frustration Rozia had never understood.

Stepmother nodded.

"Why didn't you hit me that time?"

Stepmother looked away and a frown creased her forehead. "I never forgot that day. I got to the fence and something made me stop. I don't know, like somebody was telling me to go back. When

I went back to the house and saw you crying to your mother"-- She shrugged. "I just couldn't hit you then. I don't know what craziness I went through in those years, Rozia. But I never forgot that day."

A burst of laughter came from Vick and Lena's corner of the room, and Rozia smiled, although she had no idea what they were laughing about. But she felt warm and happy. Her mother had interceded for her. Prayers were answered and she and her stepmother were finally at peace with each other.

XIX

Later one protests: How did we get here
This way...
And is it all right for the children to listen,
For the weeds slanting inward, for the cold mice
Until dawn?

~ John Ashbery

Rozia found that she was pregnant yet again. "Please Lord, not now," she prayed. It was no surprise to her that her latest pregnancy was not the happiest news to either Vick or his mother.

"You're having too many babies too fast," Anna said bluntly when she heard of Rozia's condition. "There must be something you can do. Go talk to the priest."

"I can't talk to the priest," Rozia protested. "What can a priest do?"

Anna went to the priest herself. "If your son is having too many children, then they should not have so much sex," the priest said.

Anna came home and indignantly reported the priest's words. "Women shouldn't have to have babies one after another," she fumed. "Those priests don't have to raise kids."

After Anna's words with the priest, delivered in Polish, Rozia seethed with humiliation and resentment. Anna had no right to talk to someone outside her marriage about family. Her mother-in-law sounded as bad as that Margaret Sanger, who actually started a birth control clinic, as if was her business to decide what babies would be born instead of God's. On the other hand, the priest made it sound like Rozia's condition was her own fault. She had done nothing but

Anna Trombley's house where Rozia lived
in her first years of marriage.

submit to a husband's rights. Having sex was not her idea. But she kept her thoughts to herself. She was not about to talk to Vick's mother about what went on in the bedroom.

At least the children hadn't understood the exchange. Although everyone in the neighborhood understood Polish, Rozia's children never knew the language. Rozia still remembered getting her hands rapped with a ruler for speaking Polish, and the only time she spoke Polish around the house were the times she had to tell Vick something that she did not want little ears to hear, or when anger got the best of her.

"Mama, the A&P wagon is here," Roseanne interrupted her thoughts. Rozia dropped the handle of the butter churn and went to the door. They didn't have any coffee this morning and Rozia without coffee was like Vick without chewing tobacco.

"Need anything today, Mrs. Trombley?" the driver called from his wagon, not bothering to get down. The peddler had already traveled several miles, and most of the farmers, even if they only bought a few items, were glad to see him.

"We ran out of coffee this morning, Mr. Steinbaum," Rozia called out from the front door. "Wait. Please." Rozia found the peddlers convenient and she even bought Vick's work shirts and the girls' black stockings from peddlers.

Rozia ran to the bedroom and slipped on her shoes. Shoes were not something she wore around the house. She didn't have anything left from her grocery money, so she took Vick's billfold out of its hiding place..

The following Saturday, Vick stormed into the kitchen, his blue eyes blazing. "You went into my billfold!" he roared.

Rozia stared at him. She had forgotten to tell him about the A&P wagon last week. "I bought some coffee," she finally said.

"I went to Crump for a mower part, and I didn't have enough. You stole my money."

"I didn't steal it!" Rozia blazed. She was not a thief. "I forgot to tell you. Five dollars a month doesn't stretch far enough anymore. I needed to buy the coffee."

"Five dollars it is," Vick yelled, shaking the billfold at her. "Don't you ever touch my money again!"

"Psha Krew!" (dog's blood) she spat, "I work around here too!"

"You're just like your aunt. You conniving women are all alike. Now I owe for a damn mower part." He slammed out the door. He kept his billfold in his pocket after that.

Rozia burned. Her Aunt Tillie, Tata's sister, had helped herself to Vick's uncle Frank Nowak's money when he was treasurer of the Polish Alliance, and Frank had to find a way to replace his wife's indiscretion. It wasn't the first time Vick compared her to members of her family and the comparisons were never good ones.

She also felt a prick of guilt. If she would forego her coffee and Vick his tobacco, maybe they could afford better stockings for the girls, although she knew the girls hated those stockings. Soon they would be in school and rolling them down to hide them. She felt bad about that; she knew how it was to be on the wrong side of fashion at school, but it was all they could afford. Somehow, she would squeeze her pennies and order from the Sears Roebuck Catalog this Christmas. Although they didn't order much from the Bible-sized catalog, Rozia still loved looking through it, and it came in handy in other ways too. The girls cut it up for paper dolls and one year Rozia cut out pictures and letters and Vick made blocks for Ed when he was learning his alphabet. And when it was outdated, it came in handy in the outhouse.

Alice was born the following December in 1930 three days before Christmas. By the time young Ed started school at Cherry

School, he had three sisters and a brother. How had the time flown that her first baby was not a baby anymore, but a serious little man, seven years old. Their dog, Old Pup, had watched over him more than she had, Rozia thought. Once, when Ed was supposed to be old enough to use the outdoor toilet, he slipped down into the cut-out hole and hung there. Old Pup had come to the kitchen door and barked and danced towards the toilet until Rozia followed the dog and found her little boy hanging to the toilet hole ready to fall in. Another time Ed had wandered out into a tall field of grain and couldn't find his way back and Old Pup kept circling back to the house so that the toddler would follow him. Now her Eddie was in school and he was in love with his teacher. He came home from school and asked Rose why she didn't dress like Miss Colliker, why she didn't fix her hair like Miss Colliker. How did other women her age handle babies that grew so fast? How did they handle housework and farm work and have any time for the babies?

That summer Rozia tried visiting Verna Jankowski, the girl who had insisted on being her friend back in their school days. Now Roazia was the one who needed a friend, and she hoped the years had altered Verna since she had married Art Siegu. Rozia found that Verna took pregnancy far more easily than Rozia ever had. She had delivered her last baby in the morning and planted potatoes in the afternoon, but Rozia saw that Verna was as impervious to everything else as well. Her house was infested with flies. They crawled over her kitchen table, they filled the kitchen door. Rozia went home and didn't go back. Everyone had flies, but not like that.

XX

Someone will have to weed and spread
The young sprouts. Sprinkle them in the hour
When shadow falls across their bed.

~ W.D. Snodgrass

Even more than the increasing pressure of her married life after Alice's birth, Rozia found that she could not do what she had done in the earlier years of her marriage. She had always felt pressure to do more, but she always tried to do more. Now she felt tired, always tired. One day when she was baking bread and Beattie stopped to visit, Rozia couldn't handle the heavy dough, and Beattie took over and kneaded it and shaped it into fat loaves to rise. "You'd better go to Doctor Drummond, Rozia," Beattie said. "You're as weak as a kitten."

Rozia sat down heavily in a chair by the kitchen table. "You know how Vick feels about doctors," she said wearily. She hadn't been able to deliver any of her babies without a doctor's help, which was an added financial drain that Rozia felt responsible for.

"I don't care what Vick says," Beattie said. "Even after your babies, you should have more of your strength back."

Shortly after Beatties's visit, Aunt Eva Glancy told Rozia about a county health clinic that had opened up. Rozia could go free. Rozia knew that Beattie was right and she went.

Although national disease monitoring was first conducted as early as 1850, and the federal government knew that the Spanish influenza had killed 50 million people between 1919 and 1920, public health in that day was still in its infancy, but it had been growing since the early

1900's to curb diseases associated with poor nutrition, poor maternal and infant health and diseases such as tuberculosis. Between 1914-1933, the Rockefeller Foundation provided $2.6 million to support county health, although many other nongovernmental public health initiatives had already started and were supported by groups such as the National Tuberculosis Association. By 1900, 40 states had health boards that made advancements in sanitation and microbial science information available to the public, but county departments of health did not arise until after 1911. By 1931, county health departments were providing services to one fifth of the U.S. population. Rozia was lucky enough to have access to one.

When she came back home from her visit, she was reeling with what the doctor had said. Her lungs were peppered with the dreaded TB bacilli, the same disease that had killed her mother and her aunt. Now she had signs of the same disease, and she had five children to care for.

When Rozia got home, Anna had already fixed supper, and the family was at the table. The smell of fried potatoes and side pork turned Rozia's stomach. Well, she wasn't pregnant this time anyway. The food smell was just another part of her life that now seemed out of control. She slipped past the supper table and went to the bedroom to change her clothes. When she came out, the kids had scattered and Anna was clearing the table. "Aren't you going to eat?" she asked.

"No Ma, I'm not hungry." Rozia had taken to calling Anna Ma, as Vick did.

"Well, what did the doctor say?"

Rozia looked from Anna to Vick. "He said my lungs are peppered with signs of TB. He said to rest a lot and not kiss the kids."

Vick snorted and Anna laughed. "Damn fool doctors," she said. "That's a crazy cure."

Rozia looked at Vick. "What do you think?" she asked.

"You don't look sick," he said.

Rozia would not cry in front of these two. She pressed her lips together to keep them from trembling and picked up the bowl of table scraps to take out to the dog. When she was outside, she took a deep breath and looked past their yard to the fields beyond. So that's all they thought of her. Her own kids were at risk, and they didn't even care. She was no good to anybody.

The following week she asked her brother, Joe, to give her a ride to Bay City. Her baby brother, had married his Theresa and was happily raising a growing family in the area. He would not ask her a lot of questions. She packed a bag of clothes and left a note. There was an orphanage on Columbus Street that advertised in the Bay City Times for help. She would work for room and board. That was all she needed. She told Vick and Anna in her note that anywhere she would work would be easier than what she had at home. It would be the closest to rest that the doctor had prescribed, and she would be working in the laundry away from the children there.

The orphanage was happy to hire her. Rozia busied herself with the laundry, with the meals, with the cleaning. She managed well enough, although she was tired after the day's work. But she slept well and she refused to think about why she was here and what she would do next.

One night she heard the director talking about her to a nurse. He didn't realize that voices traveled up the register pipe from the office to her room as clearly as if it was a telephone line. "That Rozia is different," the director said. "She has children of her own somewhere, I'm sure of it. A family in trouble, I would bet."

The other murmured an assent.

Rozia stared out the window at the stars. A family in trouble. She burned with shame to think she was part of a family in trouble.

When Rozia was still a teen, Grandma Sczygiel went back to Poland and left Rozia a small house in Bay City. Rozia had sold it and Vick used the money for bills. She wished she had the house now. A fortune teller had told Grandma that soldiers hid gold behind their barn back in Poland, and Grandma Siegu made Grandpa take her back to find it. "Psha krew," Grandpa swore at her in Polish, but he went back, and now they had hardly enough to eat over there. Vick would say Rozia's Grandma was worse than Aunt Tillie. Maybe her family was always a family in trouble. Maybe Vick was right. She couldn't cry. She couldn't even think. She didn't want to think. She turned back the covers and crawled into bed. How had it come to this?

A few days later, the director summoned her. "Rozia, someone is at the front door to see you." When Rozia went to the front hall, Vick stood there, looking strangely out-of-place wearing his Sunday clothes in the middle of the week, his stocky figure looking small in the shiny institutional hall.

"Could you come outside a minute?" he asked.

Rozia followed him without a word. The kids, all of them, even baby Alice sat in the car. Her heart turned over.

"I'm sorry I laughed about the doctor. Ma says she's not going to raise our kids. Come back home."

Rozia looked at Vick and then at her five children inside the car. What had been started must be finished. These few weeks were a strange interlude, and all the time, she knew what she would eventually have to do. "I'll go get my things," she said.

XXI

I had come to the house, in a cave of trees,
Facing a sheer sky.
Everything moved-

~ Louise Bogan

Vick had seven mouths to feed on forty acres, and barely made enough to pay taxes after the stock market crashed in New York. As with all things of national significance, it took a while to feel the tremors in Beaver township, but the price of their cash crops had fallen to nothing. Rozia appreciated the daily paper and magazines that Anna subscribed to. At home, growing up, they never had a subscription to anything at all. Tata's news came from newspapers passed around at work or told to him by someone who had a newspaper of their own.

Rozia looked forward to a Sunday afternoon reading, but as often as not, Vick called from the porch, "Put down that reading and come and sit on the swing with me." He looked over the papers in the evening on the day they arrived and skipped reading half of them. Rozia wanted to read every page, but she never got the chance to read during the week. She itched to spend the day reading, reading, reading. But she reluctantly pushed the papers back into the closet and went out to the porch.

"Vick, this depression sounds serious," she told him one Sunday. "People are losing their homes in the cities." She remembered too well Amelia Klinsky and her jobless husband.

Vick rocked the swing and chewed on his Red Man tobacco,

a frown creasing his heavy brows. His dark hair was beginning to recede on his forehead, and the lines around his mouth had deepened. He wore his Sunday shirt until chore time on Sundays, but the collar was frayed and he didn't have another. "We've just got to keep the taxes paid," he said. "We've got enough to eat."

"But Floyd and Gert," Rozia said.

They rocked silently. Anna was out on the lawn turning somersaults with the kids and their happy squeals floated across the yard. I wish I had her energy, Rozia thought for the hundredth time. The doctor had told her that everyone was different, and Rozia needed to stop trying to do what her mother-in-law did, but Rozia still felt that she never measured up. Even though Vick seemed happy to have her back and she rested more often now without risking his ire, Anna's disappointment with Rozia still simmered. Rozia suspected that Ma had told Beattie and Gert that Vick's wife could do more if she tried. Both had cooled toward her, and Rozia felt like she had in her school years when she never quite fit.

As the year crept closer to tax time, Rozia's head was churning while she hung out the wash in the cold autumn sunshine. As Vick had predicted, they managed to store up enough to eat, but Rozia knew the money Vick saved in his billfold was not enough for taxes. Taxes had to be paid. Others had lost farms. 'Lord and Mama and Mother Mary, what will we do if we can't make it?' she prayed.

"Ma'am?" a voice startled her. She dropped the clothespin she was holding and whirled around, self-conscious. She was barefooted, as usual.

She stared at the stranger who had come out of nowhere into her back yard, a middle-aged man dressed in a suit and a tie in the middle of the week. Was he here to talk about taxes already? "Yes?" she asked abruptly.

He tipped his hat politely. "I see you have some chickens, Ma'am. I'm Jewish and our holidays are coming. I would like to buy your chickens. Would you take a dollar apiece?"

Rozia forgot her bare feet. A dollar apiece! The man was a Jewish angel, an answer to her prayers. "Wait," she said. "I'll get my husband." She went around the clothesline and ran for the barn. They would make it through this year after all.

But as the depression deepened, Gert and Floyd were not so lucky. They lost their jobs and their home in Flint. Together with their two boys, they moved in with Vick and Rozia. In spite of their bad luck, Gert cheerfully helped out around the place and said a depression doesn't go on forever. She had already lived through rough years. But Floyd was unaccustomed to farm life and a farmer's diet. He couldn't help with the chores, and he often didn't eat what the family ate. Gert ignored him, but he made Rozia uncomfortable. She was relieved when, after a few months, they found a place back in the city.

Vick and Rosia continued making ends meet on the forty-acre farm until one day in 1932 Anna came back from Beattie's unexpectedly. "Good news!" she said that evening at supper.

Rozia reached over and rescued young Alice's milk cup which threatened to tip off the table. She had learned to listen to news of any kind while fending off minor catastrophes.

"124 acres of land for sale! It even has buildings on it!"

"Where?" Vick asked suspiciously.

"Where, he asks," Anna said as if she didn't know Vick's opinions. "In Arenac County of course. Right down the road from Frank's." Vick's Uncle Frank and Rozia's Aunt Tillie had moved to Arenac County back in 1912, and Vick thought Rozia's Aunt Tillie had probably convinced his uncle to buy a farm in the middle of nowhere.

Anna continued, "This neighbor of theirs, John Youngman, wants to sell, and sell quick, to buy his niece a ticket back to Germany."

Alice's milk tipped anyway and Rozia jumped up for the dishrag. "Quit playing and eat your supper," she scolded.

Young Ed looked interested. "Why does he want to sell a whole farm just to buy a ticket for his niece?" he asked.

Anna laughed. "My question exactly, Eddie. The niece's husband is abusing her, and she wants to get as far away as she can get. I guess Youngman bought the farm in partnership with the girl's father, but I think he died, so maybe Youngman feels he has to look out for her. One thing I know. The farm is cheap."

"Uncleared?" Vick asked.

"Yes," admitted Anna, "but it's good land, Vick. The Rifle River follows the back line."

"Even cheap is too much for 124 acres," Vick said abruptly and got up from the table. Ed followed him out the door.

"They have to get that young cow into the barn," Rozia said to Anna. "She still doesn't like to be milked."

Anna didn't care about Rozia's explanation. She followed Vick out the door and Rozia heard her say, "I can lend you the money, and Walt and I can go and fix up the place before you come with the kids."

He didn't answer. Rozia mopped Alice's face with the wet dishrag. Rozia had no idea how Anna had managed to squirrel away that kind of money. Although she and Vick were farming Anna's acres, she had never demanded a share of the crops, as far as Rozia knew, but Anna had a long history of handling money, something she had never shared with Rozia.

At any rate, Rozia felt Anna's excitement. A place of their own. Her own kitchen, her own castle to decorate as she had once imagined in the new Busia's toilet years ago. But Vick could be stubborn. He had never been in anyone's debt in his life.

That night in bed, Rozia said, "We could do it, Vick."

"Remember the time I drove out there to Uncle Frank's to pick up the Guernsey calf?"

"Yes." Vick had taken Ed, who was only eighteen months old then. Vick had driven home with the calf in the back seat of the car. But that was years ago. When Uncle Frank had moved to Arenac, he tried to raise sheep on his new farm, and according to Aunt Tillie's letters, Frank had slept in the barn with his sheep when they were birthing lambs. It seemed a hard place to live but, on the other hand, they had brought chicks and piglets into the house themselves when they were born too early.

But Vick confirmed her thoughts. "It's wild land. All I can remember was a dirt road with holes that could have swallowed a horse and trees, trees, trees."

"That was awhile ago and Beattie and Leo bought a farm there just a few years ago. Other people must be moving in as well."

. Vick had never kept it a secret that he thought Beattie's husband a foolish Dutchman. "I farmed Ma's land all this time and now she wants to send me off to the woods somewhere."

Rozia was struck at Vick's bitter words. He took his mother's offer as rejection, and Rozia well knew how that felt. But Rozia thought that Anna's offer was a little more far-sighted. Forty acres wasn't enough for the family anymore. They needed more cash crops every year besides the hay and the corn they had to grow to keep their animals fed. But this was no time to point out finances.

"A farm of your own," she said, "and three times as big."

"Yes," Vick said, "but all uncleared."

"Those first crops would run away on us," Rozia said. "I've heard of corn growing twice as high as a man."

"We'd have to work like hell," Vick said.

"I guess we're already doing that. The kids are getting older. They'll be a lot of help."

"Yes. The kids are a lot of help," he said.

Rozia smiled into the darkness. They would do it then.

Anna Trombley and brother, Walt, in front of Vick and Rozia's
new home on Hickory Island

XXII

"Hope" is the thing with feathers—
That perches in the soul—
And sings the tune without the words—
And never stops—at all—

~ Emily Dickinson

The buildings on the land Vick and Rozia bought almost daunted even the stalwart Anna. John Youngman had built a two room shelter with a loft and nothing to shield it from the weather but tar paper and a little wood burning stove. Behind Youngman's crude building, an Indian shack housed Indian Frank who didn't trust any food unless the squirrels would eat it first. He moved out when Youngman sold the place, but as far as Anna could tell, John Youngman hadn't even lived in the contrivance he had built, but boarded at the neighboring Larsen's and left Indian Frank to feed his squirrels.

Anna privately wondered about this John Youngman. He made gallons of homemade wine from wild grapes on his acreage and left it all at Beattie's but did little to clear and farm his acreage. It was a strange way to live as far as Anna was concerned, but the deed was done. Anna had coopted her brother, Walt, to come with her to make the place livable for Vick and Rozia and five kids until Vick could saw enough lumber to build something better. She papered the walls with cardboard and her brother Walt built cupboards. They were rough lumber, but they were cupboards. Anna bought an old horse to work up a garden and do heavy hauling.

The first time Vick came to his new farm, he must have been as dismayed at the house they would live in, but he only said, "That old plug looks old enough to die." Nevertheless, as the summer progressed, the old plug helped Vick and Walter with the fences around the place. The place needed fences for the cattle.

The barn came from Beaver that year. John Dominowski had built it years before when he and Rozia's cousin, Angeline, had married and intended to farm. When the couple gave up farming and moved to Bay City, Tata had bought their property, and now he gave the barn to Rozia and Vick. Mr. Kinch, an Arenac neighbor, transported the barn forty miles in pieces and boards. When it was reassembled, it was a beautiful piece of work, hip-roofed with huge wooden pegs to hold the beams together. Unfortunately, Vick was right about Anna's horse. It died before the barn was finished.

Vick and Rozia's property was originally one of the historic land grants that Abraham Lincoln had signed into law, when Vick and Rozia's parents were still in Poland, and the property had passed through a few owners, still undeveloped, before Vick and Rozia had ever heard of Arenac County. The name Arenac is a combination of 'arena' (sandy area as in a coliseum) and the Indian word 'ac' meaning 'place of', and so it means 'sandy place'. Originally it had been an outlying aggregate of Bay County, but the northern people were not happy, since their taxes were mostly used to improve Bay City. In 1883, they finally got a county of their own.

By the time Vick and Rozia arrived, the county already had a thriving community around Omer, five miles northwest of Hickory Island. Omer was born as early as 1850 in the lumber era, and had been the first county seat until 1892. Standish, the current county seat, was ten miles west of Hickory Island and also well established, but Hickory Island was still largely undeveloped, although small farms were being carved out of acres of forest. The Rifle River flooded fre-

quently and had left rich land in its wake. Vick and Rose's acres were not sandy at all.

Hickory Island was named for the plentiful hickory trees in the area, but it was not an island at all, but a part of Au Gres Township, set off on the East by the old Rifle River that ran behind Vick and Rozia's acres and the 'cut' on the West, the Rifle River that took a shorter route to Wigwam Bay. The 'cut' was made in the logging days when Jim Reeder and about fifty men decided to reroute the troublesome old river, and the deed was done in one night of dynamiting.

The river was an important part of the area's history. A historic bridge across the 'cut' on Hickory Island Road was already in place when Vick and Rose bought their farm and still stands, although it is now closed to vehicular traffic.

Vick and Rozia moved to their new home in Hickory Island, two years after they bought it: 124 acres for $2600. The kids slept in the Indian shanty that stood behind the two-room tar papered house that Anna and Walt had tried to make livable.

Vick set to work to add more living space to their new home. He used rough lumber and the new living-room and bedrooms went up quickly. The added space also added two upstairs bedrooms.

"Do it right," Rozia admonished him.

"We'll have a new house in five years," Vick said. The house was the one they lived in the rest of their lives.

When John and Mary Nowak came to visit the new farm, Mary exclaimed, "It's so lonesome out here! How do you stand it!" Back in Beaver Township, Garfield Road had been improved, the land was cleared and electricity had come through. Vick and Rozia's farm was slowly yielding to the crosscut saw, the evenings were lit by gas lamps, but in their loft bedroom at night, Rozia could hear the whippoorwill sing them to sleep through the summer nights and she was happy. Her own house, her own kitchen, their own farm.

Vick and Rozia's first five children: Alice, Roseanne, Lillian, Ed and Elmer

XXIII

And the crickets were hauling their armor
Into the weeds and dusty bushes,
...I had to put together the meaning of our neighbors.

~ Daniel Hall

Vick and Rozia's kids didn't have far to walk to school from their new home. John Youngman had donated an acre of his land to the Hickory Island School, and it was built right across the field. As the kids grew, it was obvious to Rozia that their characters grew as differently as wild flowers in the same field. Ed and Roseanne acted like two old people in young bodies. Elmer didn't study unless he was driven to it, and he teased his older brother every chance he got. But Rozia was happy for her lively son, even though he could be a handful. When he was a baby, the doctor at the clinic saw an ominous curve in his spine. When Elmer didn't walk on time, the clinic sent Rozia to Detroit with her baby for further testing. The doctors there warned her that the curvature was incurable and he would probably never walk.

Rozia brought him home and prayed over and over again that her son would not be a cripple. She had no idea of the medical diagnosis. She just took care of him and prayed, and Elmer eventually crawled and then walked and then ran. Whatever the doctors had seen, it disappeared and Elmer was one of the quickest, liveliest boys at Hickory Island School. Rozia's prayers changed to ones of thanks.

Lillian was the pretty one, an easy-going, eager-to-please girl that balanced her serious older brother and sister and the lively

Elmer, liked by everyone. And Alice was the moody one. Her spirits went from high to low like a March day.

Whatever their characters, all of them spent most of their time out of school helping to carve out a farm of 124 acres of woods. The first years were relentless. They hoed beans and corn after the small fields were cleared; they hauled hay, milked cows, helped with bringing in the crops. The girls learned to can whatever was harvested from the garden and the boys helped with killing the animals that fed them through the long winter months.

Their hard work was paying off. When Uncle Mike visited, he shook his head in admiration at the shelves of canned fruits and vegetables and the crocks of side pork and sauerkraut. "You are a good gustabini," he said—a good manager. Rozia treasured his words. She hadn't thought of herself good at anything in years. Vick's Uncle Leo Nowak added to Uncle Mike's praise when he came over. He admired Rozia's healthy flock of chickens. The brood hens hatched large nests of chicks and he loved to watch them cluck and bring their babies under their wings which could barely cover the lively brood.

As hard as the family worked, they always observed Sunday as a day of rest. After their five-mile trip to Omer to St. Edward's Church, Rozia kept Sunday a special day. It wasn't likely Uncle Gus and Mary would show up or Uncle Ted would drop by, but their farm always produced enough to eat, even if Rose had to occasionally take a chicken from the growing flock to add a special twist to their Sunday meal. After dinner, the kids were free to get up a game of softball or swim in the Cut, as the fast-moving Rifle River was still called. It was just a mile from Vick and Rozia's farm and the neighborhood kids quickly learned to swim. Except Roseanne. She stayed in the shallows and watched the others dive recklessly from the bank.

Rose could read in the few Sunday hours before milking time. She read the kids' school books, she read whatever she could find to read. Vick took a nap or umpired the kids' ball games or walked the fields, already organizing what needed to be done the following week.

After a couple of years, Rozia found herself drawn into her new community, so different from Beaver township. Dusty Rhodes needed a 4-H leader, and he wasn't listening to any protests from Rozia, who had five possible 4-H members in her own house.

"I can't sew," Rozia objected.

"No problem, Rose," Dusty assured her. "Just keep one step ahead of the kids. And you've got a couple of daughters who will get so much out of the program."

Even after all these years, Rozia had a hard time saying no. "I'll try," she reluctantly agreed.

Dusty grinned his satisfaction.

Rozia realized that she had not only taken on a new job, she had the English name Rose here. Although Gert and Beattie had called her Rose more often than not, this new neighborhood without Tata and her Polish neighbors gave the name a resonance that fit.

For awhile, Rose also worked as 4-H leader for the neighborhood boys. "I can't even pound a nail straight," she once again protested to Dusty.

"No problem"-- Dusty started.

"I know," Rose said, "just keep one step ahead of the kids. But only on the condition that you find somebody else soon." She had learned to cut out her own patterns and put dresses together, but she doubted whether she would ever build a birdhouse or anything else. She was relieved when Louie Tremble volunteered for the job. Or rather had it thrust upon him by the persistent Dusty.

Roseanne and Lillian learned a lot that year, and Rose was glad she had accepted Dusty's challenge. Roseanne picked up needlework with all the serious concentration she did with everything else. Her first major project, a white dress with puffed sleeves and a princess-style waistline, fit her perfectly. Rose was proud of her oldest daughter's ease with a thread and needle. She must have taken after Anna, Rose thought. Even with all the other sewing Anna did, she had already put together several quilts. Rose had made one, the Texas Star, for Dora's wedding present, and it had taken her months to do that.

Of course, the job as 4-H leader had its drawbacks. One of the neighbor girls, Nancy Locke, started using stitches on her sewing project that Rose had never seen before. The work was all handwork. A few women were lucky enough to have Singer sewing machines, but not many in Hickory Island. "My aunt told me to do it this way," Nancy said.

"But Nancy, that kind of work isn't in our 4-H book," Rose said.

"My aunt says it looks better this way," Nancy countered. Rose could see that the work was beautifully done, and Nancy insisted on finishing her stitches according to her aunt. At the final judging, the judges questioned Rose and she had to tell them that Nancy had learned the stitches from her aunt. Nancy's aunt was furious and Rose felt terrible, especially when the blue ribbon went to Roseanne.

Besides incurring the wrath of the Locke's, Leo Nowak's girls were in Rose's 4-H group and brought bedbugs into her house. Rose saw one crawl out of their pile of coats and crawl up the wall. Not wanting to embarrass them, Rose kept silent. She paid for her silence by fighting the insects for months. She finally rid the house of them with DDT. It was a new miracle remedy for countless farm pests. Rose had mixed DDT with water and painted the concoction around the outside of the house and on the barn walls to get rid of the ever-resent flies. Now she brought the smelly stuff into her house to get rid of the pests.

Actually, the bedbugs in the girls' coats should have been no surprise to Rose. Anna's younger brother's family was not like Anna. Lena, Leo's wife, was no housekeeper, and Leo, a bright man, but prone to drinking with his wife, lived in their disorganized household without comment, and ran his sawmill and even farmed a bit. He was the third of Anna's brothers who had moved to Hickory Island. After Walter helped put Vick and Rose's farm in order, he too had found a small house just down the road. Walter and other neighbors helped with projects around the farm that were too big for one man and his young boys. They helped at butchering time, and all the farmers who had grain got together and rented the threshing machine when it was time to harvest the grain, and Rose took her turn at cooking for the threshing crew when the machine was in their field.

As time went on, Rose's involvement with the Hickory Island neighborhood grew more serious. One day Mabel Lentz, director of the Hickory Island School, asked Rose if she would take over the job. Consolidation with the Au Gres School was already on the horizon, and no one in Hickory Island wanted to see that happen. Once again Rose was put into a position for which she had no relish, and once again she felt she couldn't refuse.

Hickory Island School was originally known as Au Gres No. 6, until Clark Kerr, one of the school's teachers, rechristened it. The school had already been in existence for over two decades before Vick and Rose's arrival, and was run by a local director, moderator and treasurer. It was up to this small board to contract teachers and insure that the school was equipped with its necessary supplies.

When Rose got the books from Mabel, she was shocked to find that the treasurer had been using school money. His books were a scandal, and Mabel had not wanted to turn in a neighbor. Rose had no choice but to take the matter to Mr. Noffsinger, the district superintendent.

"I'm glad you came forward with this, Mrs. Trombley," he said. "I'll give Mr. Brainard time to make this right, but it *has* to be made right. Wouldn't those people in Au Gres who want to consolidate Hickory Island have fun with this if the books were audited?"

Mr. Brainard, who lived down the road a mile, replaced the missing money, but he had to sell his place to do it. The Locke's fury over the 4-H judging was a small matter compared to how Rose felt when the Brainards moved away. She had never meant to hurt anyone, and yet someone else had been hurt by her doing what she thought was right.

Around the same time Rose found she had been the cause of Brainard's downfall, Louie Tremble, who had taken over the boys' 4-H, died. The Tremble family lived on the northern border of Vick and Rose's farm, and Rose felt that as a neighbor, she needed to do something to express sympathy. "I don't know if they will want a vigil, but if they do, I'll stay the night," she told Vick.

"Well, I won't," Vick said shortly. Tremble's horse got out many times and trampled the crops in his hard-worked fields. The only neighbors that stayed at the Tremble house that night were Ed Payne and Rose. Ed Payne lived on the end of their road and fished the bay for a living. He also had the ice house. During the winter, he chopped huge blocks of ice out of the bay and covered his harvest with layers of straw. The ice kept through most of the summer, and for a small fee, Ed provided ice to the neighborhood for their ice boxes.

As the night wore on and Nancy, Louie's wife, finally fell asleep, Rose and Ed's conversation drifted into talk of life and death. Ed was no believer. "When you die, you die like a dog," he said. "Nothing more."

Rose was shocked at her neighbor's nonbelief. Everyone she had known in her old neighborhood went to the same church she did. Many here were Protestants and some did not go to church at all. Louie's wife, Nancy, told Rose that before Louie had died, the priest had visited him regularly, but he remained a lapsed Catholic. "I lived the way I lived," Louie had said. "Why be a hypocrite now?"

After Louie's death, Nancy rode for years with Vick and Rose to St. Edward's in Omer, her French Catholic faith unshakeable.

As Vick and Rose put down their roots in their new neighborhood, Rose began to think that five children would be her family. But the year Alice turned eight, Rose found that she was pregnant once more.

XXIV

From the fixed place of Heaven she saw
Time like a pulse shake fierce
Through all the worlds. Her gaze still strove
Within the gulf to pierce its path;

~ Dante Gabriel Rossetti

"Ed! Ed, where are you?" Roseanne called as she walked around the corner of the barn. She knew where her brother's secret place was and she never bothered him there, but this was important. She had heard Mom and Dad this morning and she needed to talk to someone. Mom wouldn't tell them about the new baby– not yet anyway.

Ed sat in the straw pile, his back to her, and she didn't see that his shoulders were shaking with sobs until she was too close to leave.

He turned away from her when she sat down.

"What's the matter?"

"Nothing."

"Sure. Nothing."

He clumsily wiped away his tears and blew his nose.

She sat quietly.

"You can't tell anybody," he finally said.

She nodded.

"I want to be a priest."

She stared at him. "Well then, why are you crying?"

"Look at us. I finished the eighth grade and that's it. Dad said we don't need to go to high school. If I can't even get to high school, how can I ever get through all those years of seminary? It's impossible."

They both looked across the field at Hickory Island School, their alma mater. Ed was already two years out of school, and Roseanne had finished a year ago with nothing more in sight. She thought of her news—another baby. She felt a trace of bitterness. "We should be telling somebody. How can you find out what can be done if you don't say anything?"

"No," he said, "and you promised. Mom doesn't need something else to worry about. She's going to have another baby."

Roseanne sighed and got up from the pile of straw. "I didn't think you knew," she said.

Ed smiled in spite of himself. "I have big ears too," he said.

Arlene was born in Omer Hospital in May of 1938, and they couldn't help but love the round, happy baby. Even Ed tried his hand at hemming new diapers and they all took turns rocking her, changing her diapers and watching her for the first smile, the first time she rolled over, the first time she stood up.

For once, Vick was not dismayed with the newest addition to the family. "She'll be a help to you," he said to Rose. He didn't know how prophetic his words were.

When Arlene was born, Hickory Island still did not have electricity and it was a struggle to keep the baby's milk from turning sour in the summer heat. Likewise, it was a struggle for Roseanne to keep her promise to Ed. But one day, as she and Rose were pitting cherries and they had the kitchen to themselves, she said, "Mom, is it ever okay to break a promise?"

Rose frowned at the pan of red fruit. "How do you mean?" she asked. It was best not give hasty answers to such questions.

"Remember the time Ed and I were in Leonard Nowak's woods

picking berries and his bull chased us and Ed climbed the tree but I ran for home?"

Rose smiled. "Yes, he would have been up there half the night if you didn't tell us where he was."

"He didn't want me to tell. He yelled he could get down by himself."

"Well, you did right by telling that," Rose said.

"Ed wants to be a priest, but he said not to tell," Roseanne blurted.

Rose stared at her flushed daughter. Rose had taught them how important it was to keep their word. Thank God, Roseanne saw the bigger picture this time, but Rose couldn't think what to make of this news. Ed was a quiet, dutiful boy, but a priest? Nobody she knew wanted to be a priest. How could he be a priest? "Well, you did right by telling that too," Rose finally said.

"Ed has to go to high school."

"Yes," Rose said. The high school in Omer was five miles away. Vick would never agree.

With a single-mindedness that surprised her, Rose argued for Ed to start high school and start it immediately. He had already lost two years. Anna joined in the argument. "I remember one time way back when he was a kid swinging on the gate," Anna said, "Eddie told Rose and me he was going to help us get to Heaven. I think that's what he's meant to be."

Rose was grateful for Anna's support. Vick finally acquiesced.

Then Roseanne wanted to go to high school too. If Ed went to high school, she should be able to go. so she could be a nurse. What was Vick to do? It couldn't be much different than the years at Hickory Island School. They still helped out with the farm work. The wall was breached. All of their children would finish high school, something that few in Vick and Rose's generation had ever thought possible or even necessary.

But Rose soon noticed the difference. The kids were older, they had to study more. Vick listened to the battery radio every night and in the small house, it was impossible for the kids to do their homework in quiet. The crush of family was beginning to strain their lives in far different ways than their years in Beaver Township. When they lived at Anna's, there were three bedrooms upstairs and one downstairs, and the rooms were bigger. Here, they had a small bedroom for the girls and a small bedroom for the boys and neither room had more than a bed and a dresser. Every sound in the small house was loud and clear.

Vick didn't like Rose's crusade to give the kids more space in the house than he had. School was school. House was not more school. In spite of the restricted space and time, both Ed and Roseanne finished high school in three years.

Vick and Rose's barn transported from Beaver Township
and erected in 1932.

XXV

Love, Hope, and Self-esteem, like clouds depart
And come for some uncertain moments lent.

~ Percy Bysshe Shelley

Vick became increasingly silent in those tension-filled years, his silences only relieved with bursts of thunderous anger. Never a social couple, he and Rose now saw few people their own age. Relatives from their old neighborhood visited rarely. The happy-go-lucky Uncle Ted of Vick's young years stopped in occasionally. He had married Mary from Chicago and neither Vick nor Rose liked her or her brood of seven children who descended like locusts on Sunday afternoons. Vick especially abhorred Mary's bossiness. She would interrupt her own incessant monologues to call, "Theodore, change the baby's pants." And to Vick's disgust, Ted would comply. It was a long way from the way women should act, and Rose's insistence on the kids going to high school and turning down the radio during homework time came close to the same thing.

One day Vick was loading manure in the barnyard, and the cows kept trying to climb on the pile. Vick yelled and Old Pup started chasing the cows around and around the locked barnyard. Vick's yells increased and so did the dog's frenzy.

Rose ran out and found Vick in a paroxysm of anger.

"Stop yelling," she yelled herself. "Can't you see the dog thinks you want him to chase them?"

Vick glared at her, his blue eyes glazed with anger.

"Pup, come here, Pup," Rose called. The dog hesitated and then came loping back to the fence. Rose turned toward the house and saw Mrs. Larsen, their neighbor across two fields, coming down the driveway.

"I heard yelling from my place," she panted. "Is something wrong?"

Rose's face burned. "No, it was just the cows. Vick couldn't get them away from the manure pile," she said.

Her neighbor gave her an odd look and Rose was mortified. Mrs. Larsen was no fool, but Rose had learned, for pride's sake, to act like everything was under control.

"Now that you're here, come in and have some coffee," she said, "and tell me one more time how you do your pie crusts."

Mrs. Larsen followed Rose into the kitchen.

"Don't mind my messy house," Rose apologized. It seemed their small space was always crowded with undone projects.

Mrs. Larsen laughed. "Now Rose, I didn't run over here to see your house. If you keep the middle of the floor swept, the dishes washed, and your shoes on, nobody notices the dust under the bed."

Easy for her to say with her white starched apron and no one to chase after, Rose thought ruefully, looking down at her own bare feet.

When Mrs. Larsen was gone, Rose went back to peeling apples, still upset. It seemed that no matter what she saw needed doing, Vick's wall of silence or anger were the only reply she got. What had gone wrong? She was becoming a nag, urging and repeating and demanding, but she didn't know what else to do to get Vick to move ahead of the changes their family had thrust on them.

Arenac County was changing. The push to consolidate the small country schools continued and, after three years of struggle,

Hickory Island School closed in 1941 and annexed to Au Gres city school. When Rose took over as director of the school, she inherited a box of old records and found that John Youngman had never recorded the deed for the acre of property he had donated. If the school ever closed, the deed for the acre would revert back to the farm. The lawyer for Au Gres, Mr. Sternberg, could not find the unrecorded deed, but Rose knew where it was, and she kept it to herself throughout the meetings over annexation. But Vick, worried about the legality of their holding it, went to Standish and recorded it. When the district voted to consolidate, the district snatched up the deed as their property. Rozia was angry. She knew John Youngman's wishes were not being honored. The district did not have a right to the acre. O'Keefe, the prosecutor at the time, went to court with her, although he said there was little chance for a winning verdict. It cost Vick and Rose $50 to buy the acre back that John Youngman had meant to be theirs.

But 1941 also brought electricity to Hickory Island, and Vick and Rose bought a Kelvinator refrigerator, which lasted them the rest of their lives. Rose could make homemade ice cream for Sunday dinner dessert. And shortly after the Kelvinator, Vick bought an electric radio so he could hear the Detroit Tigers ball games. He loved listening to the ball games and even when he was out in the field and Rozia was in the house, she kept the game on and went out to report the score to him.

Their first radio was struck by lightning that burned the living room curtain and sent a blue ball of fire into the room. Rozia was terrified, and electricity and thunderstorms left Rose uneasy ever after, even after the house was 'grounded', whatever that meant. But the advantages of the new radio overcame her fear. They could hear the news from Gabriel Heater. On Saturday nights Vick listened to The Grand Ole Opry all the way from Nashville, Tennessee, and on Sundays "The Greatest Story Ever Told," dramatized New Testament Bible stories.

The family was changing, the county was changing, the world was changing. Vick was not accepting change easily and Rose was at a loss to confront his retreat into silence or anger.

XXVI

How much of the things of this world
have darkened while we were inside...

~ Deborah Greyer

Arlene was four years old Anna bought Mrs. Larsen's farm next door and Rose found she was pregnant once again. Rose greeted both Anna's move and her pregnancy with mixed feelings. Ma had helped them a lot, but she was an indomitable force, and Rose did not want one more pressure on her marriage. Another pregnancy was pressure enough when she thought Arlene would be her last baby.

It was not a good time to bring another life into the world. Japan had bombed Pearl Harbor in December, and the United States was again gripped in a world war. Rose, ever alert now to the forces that swept over their family, was scared. Ed would graduate in the spring. Would he be the next Jerome Edward Trombley to die far from home? Would her screams of grief be heard all over the neighborhood as Anna's had been? Ed was graduating as class valedictorian and would be entering the seminary in September. They couldn't take him for war. He didn't have a fighting bone in his body.

The winter after Anna moved, Vick worked at renovating her house. Mrs. Larsen had covered the walls with cardboard and papered over them. Vick tore out the cardboard and put up wall board, and then added cupboards and shelves to the ill-equipped kitchen. He spent all his extra time there whenever his own work was done, and farm work was done faster during the winter months. Rose had to send Alice to get Vick on a snowy Sunday afternoon

Vick and Rose's last three children, Tom, Marylou and Arlene.

when her contractions started for her seventh baby. Marylou was born at Omer Hospital on February 10th, 1942.

Marylou was not the happy, round-faced baby Arlene had been. Ed had already left home, and the girls rocked the baby and helped with the ever-present pile of diapers when they could, but both had to finish high school, and a squalling baby in the crowded house was an added chore. Rose tried to balance what each of her children needed when she had time to think, but the year was a blur. She didn't even have time to get rid of the diaper pail when she found herself pregnant yet again.

She tried to accept this as another gift of life from God, but reality was hard. Vick was close to fifty, and they were looking at several more years of children in the house. How would she care for these youngest for another eighteen years? Already forty-two and worn from past pregnancies, she could hardly walk in her last weeks. When she tried to take a quart of milk to Anna's, she had to crawl home. After that, Alice, then Arlene, and finally Marylou delivered their Grandma Anna's quart of milk by leaving it in her mailbox after the evening milking.

Tom was born June 10th, 1943. During Rose's delivery and recuperation at Omer hospital, the whole family came down with the measles. Everyone but Vick and Alice were sick. Marylou, entrusted to Lillian's care, would not stay indoors to protect her eyes, as Rose had instructed, so Lillian put a wide straw hat on the toddler and let her outside. Marylou, a wan and skinny sight with the oversized straw hat, was the first thing Rose saw when she brought her last baby home. Rose wanted to cry for Lillian, for Marylou, for all of them, but this was no time for tears.

Rose didn't recover well after Tom's birth. Her lungs had been peppered with signs of TB after she delivered Alice, but the lung disease that had killed her mother and Aunt Antoinette had somehow healed and scarred over, and she had almost forgotten that time in the years at Hickory Island. But now Rose's body was turning traitor again, and it frightened her. She had so little energy. Had the dreaded disease come to take her away after all? Her teeth, which were never good, finally had to be pulled. She was afraid to ask Vick to return to the dentist several times and persuaded the dentist to pull all of them at once and then endured a mouth of pain and two months of toothlessness before she got her dentures.

Besides the youngest to care for, the oldest children were growing up in a far different world than the one Rose remembered when she went to Detroit and she couldn't keep up with how fast her oldest children moved out into that world. Ed had already entered the seminary and Roseanne graduated the year Tom was born and started nurse's training at Mercy Hospital in Bay City. Lillian graduated the following year and found a job in Bay City and she and Roseanne roomed together. Elmer was finishing his last year of high school, although he was not following in Ed's footsteps. He could tell the math teacher how to work out an equation so the class could understand it, but he didn't follow rules, either at home or at school. Alice was a year behind him, and she couldn't have told her math teachers anything about equations, but at least she didn't challenge them at every turn.

Meanwhile, World War II fever swept over the country. In spite of rationing, almost everyone felt compelled to do something for the cause. Alice gathered tin cans, paper, old tires, anything for the war effort. She even collected cattails. The fluff that blew their ripe seeds could be used in life vests. It seemed the war machine recycled all sorts of things that once ended up in a junk pile. Alice had her own agenda, even if it wasn't at school.

But Vick refused to deliver her collection. "The last war took my brother. To hell with them and their wars," he said. Vick's bitterness over his brother's death in World War I was still alive and adamant.

"Psha krew," Rose swore. "This isn't twenty years ago! The Nazis will take over the world if they aren't stopped. They already took Poland and France."

Vick was not going to change his mind, and Rose couldn't drive the car and haul the stuff herself, and so she fell silent. After all, she had never lost a brother to a war, and her son was safe from the draft while other boys went. The next spring the cache Alice had collected was ruined by a flood. Every few years, the Rifle River's ice jammed as it swept toward the bay and flooded Hickory Island. Sometimes the water only covered a few fields and roads, but a few times the water had crept into their yard and outbuildings. Rose had to burn the debris that Alice had collected.

XXVII

When lilacs last in the dooryard bloom'd,
And the great star early droop'd in the
western sky in the night,
I mourn'd, and yet shall mourn with
ever-returning spring.

~ WALT WHITMAN

On January 20th, 1946, Lillian brought home the first romance in the family. She was only twenty, but she was the prettiest of Rose's oldest daughters, and had already had one ill-fated romance with Art Tremble. This time it was different. Lillian did not bring a young man home just for any Sunday visit. She and Norbert intended to marry. Lillian was so young, but it would not be long before she and Vick would have a son-in-law. They would have grandkids before their youngest were out of grade school. Rose made sure the mashed potatoes were creamy, the squash was golden, the dill pickles were snappy and the chicken was browned to perfection. Norbert complimented Rose's efforts and seemed at ease with them, and the afternoon passed swiftly.

As Lillian and Norbert were leaving, it was already dark, but Lillian announced that they planned on stopping to see Grandma Anna before they went back to Bay City. Snow already covered the ground and big snowflakes began falling as Rose stood in the door and hugged herself against the cold to see them off. She waved and smiled when Lillian pointed at Norbert and called, "Yes Ma, he's driving," before she climbed into the black Ford.

Lillian had recently learned to drive, and Rose couldn't

understand her daughter's fascination with this new skill. Neither Roseanne nor Alice shared their sister's enthusiasm for cars, and as far as Rose was concerned, that was a good thing. Mechanical stuff was best left for men. Once, Anna had tried to drive. She had taken Vick's car out in the field and put it in gear, but unfortunately, she forgot how to stop the thing and ran into a fence and pushed the car all the way back to the shed. She never tried to drive again. Rose had never even tried.

When the car lights had disappeared down the road, Rose turned from the door. "Okay, you kids," she announced to Marylou and Tom who were crawling under the kitchen table chasing imaginary bears. "Get your pajamas on. It's time for bed."

She hoped they would settle down and go to bed easily. They had picked up the excitement of a possible new addition to the family. Norbert even kissed Marylou good-bye, and Rose could see her delight that a grown man with a mustache had kissed her. She was ready to play all night. But they fell asleep easier than Rose expected and when they were settled, Rose took off her shoes and went into the living room. The room now had a new couch and chair that Lillian had bought, and Rose felt a little prick of pride. The small room looked well-kept. It would have made a good impression on Lillian's young man. The radio was on and Rose let it go until Vick got up and went to bed.

Elmer and Alice had gone to the movies in Standish, and the house was quiet. It was one more way she and Vick differed. Rose loved the night and Vick went to bed with the chickens. But tonight Vick didn't object to her keeping vigil for Elmer and Alice's return. As usual, he didn't say much, but Rose could see that he was contented with Lillian's man.

She opened the paper she hadn't been able to read for the last two days. She didn't know how long she sat that way when she heard a knock at the door. She glanced at the clock and saw that it was nearly midnight. She must have dozed over the news print that was getting too small for her to see without concentrating.

A state policeman stood there when she opened the door and with him, Mr. Savage, the undertaker in Standish, which made no sense at all.

"Mrs. Trombley, there's been an accident," the policeman said.

Rose looked past him to see Elmer's car drive in through the slowly falling snow, the car Grandma Anna had bought and then given him. Did he hit a deer? The car was still running. "It couldn't have been too bad," she said aloud, as she watched Elmer and Alice climb out of the car and walk towards them through the snow.

Elmer looked from the uniformed policeman to Mr. Savage to Rose. "It's not me, Ma," he said.

Vick, awakened by the voices, stood silently behind Rose, his pants hastily pulled over his long johns. Mr. Savage looked at him. "It's your daughter, Lillian," he said.

The family watched him, not saying a word.

"I'm so sorry," Mr. Savage said. "She and her friend were killed in an accident." She hardly heard the policeman recount the details.

The men, Vick behind her, the house, the world—Nothing was real. Everything was sucked up in a vacuum of disbelief. Lillian had been driving. Why had she been driving? Didn't she tell Rose that Norbert was driving? Had she coaxed Norbert to let her drive after they stopped to visit Grandma Anna? A car full of young men teased her by slowing down until she tried to pass and then speeded up. At her last attempt to pass them, she hit black ice and the car crashed into a tree. The tree was close to the Bay City State Police post. They were almost back to Lillian's apartment. Another few miles and Lillian would have been safe.

Rose didn't scream as Anna had when she heard of her son's

death. She didn't cry. She just froze, and in the next days, she did not sleep, she did not cry, she did not eat. Everything around her stopped around those words, 'killed in an accident'.

Mr. Savage identified Lillian's body and refused to let them see her until they brought the casket to the house to set it in the downstairs bedroom that Vick had added just a few years earlier. Rose remembered Arlene holding on to Lillian's hand when they were using Vick's two-by-fours as a balancing beam and Lillian's laughter when four-year-old Arlene said, "Give me your hand, Lillian, you might fall."

On the day of the funeral, the weather was terrible. Vick fainted when they carried Lillian's casket out of the house, and Rose could not remember who brought him around or anything else that day. Killed in an accident. Gladys Payne, a neighbor and sister-in-law to Ed Payne, stayed at the house and took over Rose's kitchen and organized the food and everything else donated to the family. Gladys also kept Marylou and Tom with her on the day of the funeral. The family was in no condition to watch a couple of preschoolers. The kids had been kept upstairs with Alice through a lot of the wake, but they came down and knelt by the casket to say a prayer for their big sister, although they didn't know what had happened and Rose was too stricken to notice. All she noticed was that Lillian's hair was not fixed like she had worn it. Such a small, stupid thing to notice, she thought later.

On a subzero night after the funeral, Rose saw Lillian outside the window. She knew it was Lillian as sure as she was sitting in her own skin, but, in her darkest hours, she remembered her stepmother's superstitions, and thought that she too might be going crazy. Somehow Lillian at the window didn't feel crazy, but she didn't tell anyone about what she had seen. Who would she tell?

It may have been her own fear of going crazy that made her react to Anna's scolding comment, "Why did you hang that Christmas wreath outside the front door? It's a sign of death."

"That's a silly superstition," Rose snapped.

A month after Lillian's funeral, Beattie died; Beattie the beloved, the good-natured one. She had developed leukemia some time before, and after a brief remission, she failed rapidly until the only thing between her and death was a needle and transfusions. For once, Leo and Vick agreed. The transfusions stopped and Beattie lapsed into a coma and death. On the day of her funeral, a blizzard swept the countryside, and mourners hurriedly left the gravesite before the roads became impassable. The winter was so bad that Lillian's casket stood on the grave for a week before it could be buried. Beattie's casket too stood on top of the ground until the weather abated, and the grave diggers could get through the frozen ground.

Vick and Rose visited the new graves at Saint Edward's cemetery on Memorial Day, a day as beautiful as the winter had been bleak. Rose found no joy in the blue sky and the high cumulus clouds. The gravestone that had been ordered was set in place. Rose stared at the name: Lillian May Trombley, 1926-1946. Her beautiful, sunny daughter was dead.

On the way back from Omer, Rose's pain felt like a stone on her chest. She looked up at the sky and the clouds formed a beautiful jersey cow. Rose watched it, and its serenity and beauty pressed on her sorrow until she felt like she couldn't breathe. When she got home, she barely made it to their upstairs bedroom when all the tears she couldn't cry all winter burst from her in a wild torrent that left her gasping and retching, as if she was drowning.

After that afternoon, the sorrow was still there, but the stone on her chest disappeared.

XXVIII

We wander'd together the solemn night,
(for something I know not what kept me from sleep)

~ Walt Whitman

Elmer enlisted just before his draft orders came up. Although the war was officially over, he was sent to Japan. Rose wanted to fume at Vick with a bitterness of her own. Their son was now on the other side of the world in the country that had bombed Pearl Harbor and brought thousands of families to watching the mail by day and praying by night. No matter how much Vick tried to ignore the world around them, their children had to live in that world, and it was far bigger than a small neighborhood in Arenac County.

Elmer wrote occasionally in his slapdash penmanship, and even sent photos a few times. As much as Rose could gather, his job was guarding POW's that the U.S. army hadn't yet released. He had a Japanese girl. Elmer didn't elaborate, and Rose didn't want to think what that meant. Her son was a man, a soldier in a foreign land, and she suspected his 'girl' was part of the spoils of war. She thought she had raised Elmer better than that. War was an evil thing.

Meanwhile, Alice graduated, and the younger kids had started their school days riding the red-white-and-blue school bus to Omer Elementary. Hickory Island School had been torn down after it had stood desolate and abandoned for a few years. Jamaicans used it one summer while they worked in somebody's pickle fields, but Vick and Rose did not object. Rose felt sorry for them and even fixed sandwiches a few times and took her offerings over to their little camp. After the pickle season, they left as quickly as they had appeared.

John Tremble finally tore the building down and took it away piece by piece. Vick took the poles that had supported the swings.

Although Omer was only six miles away, the two-story brick building, now an elementary school, seemed far different than the small wood frame county schools that Rose had known. Rose was finished with involvement in institutional education, and never acquainted herself with the teachers of the younger children.

When the letter finally arrived that Elmer was finished with his tour of duty in Japan, Rose cleaned and aired the house and made up his bed with the cover turned down. She put more into this homecoming than Elmer would probably notice. The day before his arrival, she went to bed, but she slept poorly. She awakened in the darkness, again wishing she could dream of Lillian. Her preoccupation with dreaming of Lillian had started months ago. She wanted to see her and hear her again, and the preoccupation worried her as much as her inability to bring her daughter to her dreamless nights.

Suddenly a voice said, "Lillian is okay now. Pray for Elmer." The voice was so clear it was as if someone had spoken to her and, as she pushed her way out from the bedcovers, she thought someone was in the house. She peered into Elmer's room, but the bed lay quiet and untouched. She went downstairs and snapped on the light. It was 1:00 a.m. Something made her walk to the calendar and point to the date and then trace slowly the days that Elmer had been traveling. She dropped to her knees by the kitchen table and prayed.

The day Elmer returned, the family was so happy that Rose almost forgot about her odd experience until sometime later when they sat around the kitchen table after dinner. Vick had gone to take Anna home. They often had Anna over for Sunday dinner after they took her to church.

"A weird thing happened on my way home from Japan," Elmer said, .gazing at his bottle of beer as if it was a memory prompter.

Rose took a small sip from her own glass and waited for him to go on. She had finally learned to drink beer without the dash of sugar she once put into it when Gert visited and insisted Rose have one.

"When we finally landed in the good ol' U.S. of A., a bunch of us went to some bar in San Francisco to celebrate." Elmer shrugged. "It seems I celebrated a bit more than the others. They finally went to get some shut eye for the rest of the trip home. By the time I left, I was pretty much the only G.I. left in the place."

"That wasn't a smart thing to do in a strange city," Rose said. She had already noticed that Elmer drank and smoked much more than she had ever caught him doing before he left home.

"It was damn stupid," Elmer agreed. "Two men attacked me, got me in an alley and beat the royal daylights out of me. As drunk as I was, that didn't take long. They took what money I had in my wallet and left me as good as dead."

"Jasne kochany!" Rose exclaimed.

"Fortunately, I had sewn much of my severance pay into an inner pocket," Elmer said. "At least I did one thing right." He looked at her and took a long drink from his beer. "You didn't need to hear all that."

"Then what happened?" Rose asked. She was not going to let him drop his story now.

"It seems some guy found me, got me to a hotel and asked the clerk to take care of me. When I revived and found that I had not only been saved, but my bill had been paid, I felt guilty as hell. I asked the manager for the man's name so that I could repay him. The manager could only tell me that the stranger told him that he walked the bars where the returning soldiers stopped to see if anyone needed help. The guy's own son was in the service, and he hoped that someone would give his son help if he needed it."

Rose remembered the strong voice that got her out of bed to pray in the middle of the night. "Lillian is okay. Pray for Elmer."

"What day did that happen?"

Elmer shrugged. "I don't know. The day I got stateside."

"What day?" Rose insisted.

Elmer went to the calendar and flipped back. When he pointed to the day, Rose felt a shiver of recognition. It was the same night she got up to pray.

She told Elmer her side of the story, but she wasn't sure that Elmer got it. He already knew that Lillian's death had ripped a piece out of their family and that his mother's answer to everything was prayer. And she could not tell her small miracle of prayer to Vick or his mother. Church was part of their lives, but little miracles weren't. Church baptized you, married you and buried you and told you how to behave.

But she could tell Tata. The next time he visited Hickory Island, he had already given his farm to Leo, his oldest son with step-mother. The farm was a mixed gift. It had several debts against it. Tata didn't visit often even when she and Vick lived in Beaver. He kept a cordial distance with Vick, and Rose had never shared her marital problems with her father. He had enough problems of his own.

When Vick and Leo wandered to the barnyard to inspect the cattle, Rose and Tata could talk, and Tata always lapsed into Polish. Although she could not tell Tata about her problems with Vick, she could tell him of her miracle prayer and he would understand. She had told him of her prayers to her mother that had been answered, and he never doubted what she told him. He was her only connection with the mother she had lost when she was seven.

XXIX

It was not I who began it...
I was nevertheless not unhappy.
...it was my life.

~ Judith Wright

One Saturday when Roseanne came home for a weekend, she looked at Rose and said, "Mom, you need to go to a doctor. Your color isn't right and you're hobbling around as if you were eighty."

"I haven't felt right since Tom was born," Rose admitted.

"Tom is already in school! You need to see a doctor."

Rose knew that Roseanne was right, but as usual, Rose had put off going to the doctor as an unneeded extra expense, but she trusted the serious young nurse Roseanne had become. Rose went to Doctor Staley in Omer the following week. He checked her into the hospital and gave her a blood transfusion. "You have to have surgery," he said. "But your blood count is low."

Rose was frightened by the thought of surgery. "I want to go home first and talk it over with my family," she said.

"Well don't take too long," Doctor Staley warned her when he signed her release.

"Take me to Bay City to Roseanne," she ordered Vick when she got back in the car.

Vick frowned, but he didn't refuse. Surgery with Doctor Staley wasn't what Vick wanted either.

When Rose got to Bay City, Roseanne didn't hesitate. She made an appointment for Rose the following day, and Vick came back to the farm alone. Doctor Mosher didn't mince words. Surgery in her condition would kill her, The blood transfusion that Doctor Staley had given her was contaminated, and she was so jaundiced, even the whites of her eyes looked yellow. Rose was hospitalized until the jaundice was cleared up.

Then Doctor Mosher told her what she had been trying to avoid. "You need a hysterectomy," he said.

Rose argued. "Then I cannot have any more children." She was not looking at the surgery as a health necessity but a certainty that there could be no more children, and nothing should be done to prevent another life from being conceived. Margaret Sanger's crusade controlling births started when Rose was a new mother, and in the years after the Second World War, Rose had read about 'French safes' that army doctors had dispensed as easily as cigarette rations.

"Mrs. Trombley, there is no way you will ever conceive another child in your condition," Dr. Mosher said. "That damaged tissue has to be removed before you have further complications."

"Please Mom, do what the doctor says," Roseanne pleaded.

"Doctors are on Margaret Sanger's side," Rose said.

"Doctor Mosher is a good Catholic doctor. He wouldn't insist if you had a choice."

Maybe Roseanne was right. She certainly felt too weak to carry another baby.

"Alice will have to take care of the kids," Rose said. "Vick doesn't cook."

"They will be fine," Roseanne said. "Just do what Doctor Mosher says."

Rose reluctantly had the hysterectomy, and her child-bearing years were over. She did feel much better after she recuperated, yet her faith in the Catholic Church was much stronger than in the medical establishment. When the 'pill' became available years later, she was against its use, and was horrified when the Supreme Court legalized abortion.

Meanwhile, the aftermath of World War II had changed the face of the nation. Rose was well aware of the different world her children would live in and she was not in favor of most of the changes. Farms were growing ever bigger, schools more centralized, families smaller and more isolated from their communities and more exposed to the world. The changes came to rural areas more slowly, but she never forgot her father's words that if she could read, she could educate herself, and she read every time she had a free minute. She read the Bay City Times, but she also read *The Catholic Weekly, The Catholic Digest* and *St. Anthony's Messenger*. She wanted to be well-informed, but she wanted her news to come from a Catholic source she could trust.

She kept Saint Edward's in Omer an important part of their family in Hickory Island. Before Ed entered the seminary, Father VanGessel taught him the Latin which Standish high school didn't offer. After Ed's entry into the seminary, Alice spent a semester at the Felician academy in Detroit before she started high school. The Felician academy was Father Frawley's idea. He succeeded Father VanGessel at Saint Edward's, and his sister was a nun at the academy. When Alice came back home, she sang in the choir, taught catechism, and instructed the youngest three in their religion, and when she graduated from Arenac Eastern, she decided to join the Victory Noll nuns in Indiana. Rose was surprised at her daughter's choice but grateful for Father Frawley's help. The church was her only reliable compass.

XXX

Nights I turn to you to hold me
but you are not there.
Am I alone?

~ Louise Gluck

In spite of her unwavering faith in her church, Rose and Vick's marriage was bleaker than ever and Rose did not know how to make it better. Vick never talked about what bothered him and if she prodded him, he either told her nothing or blew up at her and her nagging. Everything the other did, no matter how small, raised a flare of anger. Finally, overwhelmed by hopelessness, Rose said she may as well leave.

"The only way you'll leave me is with my gun," Vick said.

Rose was horrified. Could Vick mean what he said? She remembered when she was ten years old; John Kosecki had found his wife in bed with his brother and shot her. When they went to her wake, blood stained the boards of the kitchen floor where the woman had tried to escape. She still remembered the brown stain that couldn't be scrubbed out. The judge had only given Kosecki five years. He ruled it justifiable homicide.

Oddly enough, Vick and Peter Jankowski got laughing hysterically during the rosary at the Kosceki wake and had to leave the house.

Vick was not the man she thought she had married, but he was no Kosecki. In spite of his explosive rages, he had never hit her or the kids since Ed was a toddler. She didn't even remember what Ed had done, but Vick had swatted him and his big hand across the baby's bottom sent Ed flying across the room into the opposite wall. Ed sank down, his eyes big with fright, and never uttered a sound.

Rose grabbed Vick by the shoulders and shook him. "You fool!" she cried. "You dirty fool! You could kill a kid!" She ran and picked up Ed, who seemed stunned but unhurt. "Don't you ever do that again!" she hissed.

Vick stared at her, and then turned and left the room, but he had never spanked the kids again. Rose spanked when she saw fit, although sometimes she wished Vick had taken a hand to Elmer.

Alice, unbeknownst to Rose and Vick, went to Father Frawley and told him of her family's sad state of affairs, and one afternoon, Father Frawley, unannounced, showed up at the farm. Rose had to admit that she and Vick were having problems, but she was ashamed to tell all to the priest who saw their family in church every Sunday and had a son in the seminary. How had he come here? When he asked where Vick was, she sent him to the woods where Vick was cutting wood for the winter, and Vick was no more forthcoming than Rose had been. In fact, he was angry that Alice had been the one to bring Father Frawley to their doorstep, and the priest left, his visit a failure.

Perhaps the priest's visit was not a total failure after all. Rose looked to the church to help her, as it had helped her so often before. When she suggested they go and see a priest after all, Vick said he wouldn't go to Father Frawley. Despite rumors of the priest's drinking problem, Rose thought him a good man with an unfortunate weakness. Vick didn't share Rose's feelings.

Rose didn't argue. "We'll go to a priest who doesn't know us," she said. "We've got to do something, Vick."

Rose suspected that her mother-in-law had something to do with Vick finally agreeing to see the priest at Saint Florian's in Standish. Anna Trombley probably saw that their marriage was in shambles. Or perhaps Father Frawley's intervention made both of them realize that their bitterness with each other was no longer a closely-guarded family secret.

"Go see a doctor and make sure you don't have a medical problem," the priest counseled Vick. "You say your wife is crazy, but the way you two are living, I'd be crazy too. Get out of the house. See people. You're getting on one another's nerves."

The advice was terse, but oddly enough, or so Rose thought, Vick did as the priest said. In spite of Vick's stubborn silence, he followed what a priest said, Father Frawley excepted. When he was much younger and a mission priest demanded that all the men pledge that they would never swear in the Lord's name, Vick complied, and his most violent expletive from that day onward was 'Blue Lightning'.

Although the difference in neither one of them was drastic, it was better, and Vick's angry explosions abated into a more tolerant silence. And when Roseanne graduated from St. Mary's in Grand Rapids in 1948, Father Frawley lent the family his car to attend the graduation. Vick got a new Chevy the following year, and he was as proud of the car as if he had invented it himself. Rose didn't object. The Model A Ford was on its last legs (or wheels) anyway, and they had to get to church.

Ed was ordained in June of 1950 and said his first mass at St. Edward's. The parish hosted a big parish dinner for the occasion, and this time Rose was not in the kitchen, heaping the platters of chicken and bowls of mashed potatoes and yellow gravy. Father Ed's family was included as the guests of honor.

"You must be so proud," parishioners exclaimed. Rose smiled and nodded, but inside she felt guilt that anyone would think she was good enough to have brought up a priest. When Ed was only a little over a year old, he went to bed feverish and awoke in the night with such a horrible fever that huge beads of sweat stood out on his forehead. Rose sat with him and prayed over and over, "Please God, save my baby."

Before Ed ever started school and was wheeling Roseanne around in his little wagon, he threw an apple at her because she wouldn't quit crying with an earache. When Roseanne cried harder, Rose , who had seen what Ed had done, asked him why his sister was crying, he denied what he had done, and Rose told him about lying, When he had taken pumpkins from Tata's garden, she told Ed it was wrong to take other people's things. They had done so little. God had saved him and God had called him, and Rose felt that she and Vick were not really worthy to accept this day of joyful triumph as part of their own.

The Hickory Island home after renovations

XXXI

The worlds are breaking in my head
Blown by the restless wind
That comes from afar...

~ David Gascoyne

After Roseanne graduated as a registered nurse, she worked in Bay City for a few years but, like thousands of others, she was drawn to golden California. The weather was warm all year long, oranges grew like apples, and in the fifties, the state needed young workers. She left in 1951, the day after her Uncle Leo Nowak's funeral. He died of the dreaded TB, leaving Aunt Lena a widow. His large family was mostly grown, but Lena would have to depend on her two youngest boys, much as Anna had once depended on Ed and Vick. After the funeral, Roseanne threw herself on the bed and cried as if her heart was broken.

Tears were so unusual in her oldest daughter that Rose did not know how to comfort her, but Rose suspected it was not all about Uncle Leo. Roseanne was going to a strange land, a continent away from everybody she knew. Rose felt unequipped to understand Roseanne's desire to move. Her farthest move had been to Detroit, and she had relatives there to help her. Rose thought of her grandmother who had left Poland with nothing but her children and a hope that her new country would be a safer one than the one she had to leave. But what drew Roseanne to California? It was growing much as Detroit had been when Rose had moved there and jobs were plentiful, but life was more than a better job. Perhaps Roseanne's tears were a realization of that.

It was a sad leave taking, and Rose worried about her oldest daughter until they got her first letters. She wrote neat and factual letters with no sign of the sadness that Rose had seen that last day in Michigan. Roseanne had made some friends, she had found a church, she decorated her apartment with homemade curtains and plants. Rose was relieved and she had to admire Roseanne's independence. It was so different for young unmarried women now than it had been when Rose was trying to earn her own way.

Roseanne came home for her first visit in the summer of 1953. She bought a new Ford in Detroit and, with only a few hours of driving lessons, announced that she would drive the car back to California.

"It's time you had a vacation," she said to Rose. "You can go back with me and stay awhile and then I'll put you on a plane back to Michigan."

"What are you talking about?" Rose objected. "How can you drive across a whole country? You don't know how to drive."

"I know enough," Roseanne said.

"I've never been on a plane," Rose said.

"You'll love it. Your trip home will be a lot faster than our trip there." In spite of Rose's objections, she was intrigued with Roseanne's offer.

It was an adventure she never dreamed possible, and she would see places that had only been names in the newspaper. But Rose was not one to leap without looking. "I can't leave your dad here with the three kids," she worried.

Roseanne had already thought out all the objections that Rose would bring up. "They'll be fine," she said. "They're out in the field all day anyway. Get Alice to stay while we're gone. She can cook and make sure the washing's done."

Alice agreed to the arrangement, although Rose could see a

trace of resentment in her moody daughter, and Rose could hardly blame her. Alice had been asked to leave Victory Noll convent after a year. It seems the nuns thought she would do better with another vocation. She tried a few jobs without success, but the failure at Victory Noll was a bitter disappointment and living back home at 21 was doubly disappointing. Father Ed and Roseanne were well into the lives they had chosen. Even Elmer, working on the great lakes freighters, was well-employed and had a car of his own. Working for her mother was nothing but a family handout.

Rose was a little surprised that Vick didn't object to Roseanne's plan, but Vick couldn't say no to his eldest daughter, who had always been the dutiful girl who made her way and had a car even newer than his. He admired the way she went to California and talked of driving across the county as if it was a trip to Bay City. Although physically she was not like his mother (Roseanne was tall and thin), she had his mother's blue eyes and a lot of her independence. But in spite of Roseanne's determination, it was a long way to travel alone. She needed someone in the car with her on such a trip.

So Rose found herself packing a suitcase, pulled into a trans-continental adventure that she couldn't believe was happening, she who had never been away from her family except for that awful surgery. She was excited but also anxious. Since Lillian's death, she was as fearful of cars as she was of thunderstorms, and Roseanne's few hours of driver's training did not allay her fears.

Yet, she remembered the trip as a time of great beauty. When they came to the foot of a mountain pass they would drive through the next day, the hills were wild with tiny white flowers and Rose exclaimed, "The road through those flowers looks like the road to Heaven!"

She took her Kodak box camera, a gift from the kids a few years before, and she took pictures and more pictures. She wanted to capture every mile of the incredible journey. The camera had been a wonderful gift, and she appreciated the way pictures could be taken anytime she pleased. She only wished the camera could capture color. She sent colored postcards home at every stop they took.

Unfortunately, Rose's fear of cars worked against her. There were no interstate freeways, and Roseanne drove in the crush of traffic around Chicago, through narrow mountain passes, and across the desert that posted warning signs that, without proper precautions, it could be dangerous. Rose held herself so rigid that when she got to California, she had a spasm in her back and spent half of her vacation laid up to make the plane trip home.

From the letters she got from the family, even young Tom, the family was surviving in her absence. Vick even wrote once or twice and Roseanne, well-acquainted with her mother's unhappy marriage, pointed out that Vick was trying his best. In fact, in the six weeks Rose was gone, new cupboards, an inside bathroom and a new bookcase were all installed, although this was not a total surprise. She and Vick had agreed to upgrade the house before the trip was planned, and Vick kept the plan going in her absence. Their last renovation had been the year after an especially horrible flood when water had come into the house and Vick had to take a boat out to the barn to take care of the livestock. That was the year they jacked up the house and put in a cement block foundation, and Vick built a sun porch off the front door.

Rose felt bad that her fear of cars had marred Roseanne's plans. They saw some of California's scenery before Rose's back seized up, but each day trip involved California traffic which was as frightening to Rose as the transcontinental trip had been. Like the good nurse she was, Roseanne insisted Rose follow the doctor's orders to rest and said she enjoyed her mother's company just as it was. They spent evenings together talking as they had never had the chance to do before.

Rose came home to a family happy for her return and, in spite of her bout with a bad back, she felt triumphant: she, who was always afraid of skating on ice, thunderstorms, cars, and high haymows, came home on a plane that soared over mountains. Although she distrusted cars, Rose loved flying.

However she had barely landed when a tornado ripped through Michigan and killed 116 people in Flint. Her fear of storms was magnified. Gert and her boys could have been killed. Her homecoming was tainted with yet another concern, although it seemed small, compared to that day of the horrific storm when she had watched strange clouds and ordered the family to hide. Alice had not waited for Rose to come back, but left to another job, something she did not write to tell Rose and something the family had left unsaid in their letters.

Alice worked in Bay City for a short time, and then impulsively got on a train and went to California. Unlike Roseanne, she didn't know what she would do when she got there. Evidently, she figured that a job would not be hard to find. Roseanne did her best to help her moody, headstrong sister, but they did not get along well. Alice finally did find restaurant work and later a small factory job, but she did not earn enough to rent an apartment of her own. When Alice met Joe Cipolla and, after a short engagement, married him in February of 1954, Roseanne stood in her wedding. No one in Michigan could afford to be there.

Rose followed these developments through Alice and Roseanne's letters and she could only pray that Alice hadn't made a disastrous choice. Alice's choices could be impulsive, and Roseanne's assessment was not encouraging. Roseanne wasn't one to write a lot about how she felt, but she had misgivings over her sister's new husband. Joe struck Roseanne as bossy and controlling, while Alice's letters were full of rosy emotion about her Joe. It must be the way for every parent when their babies flew out of the nest. They flew and Rose could only watch.

Joe was not the first in-law brought into the family. Elmer married Dorothy Badour in September of 1953, a year before Alice's wedding. Alice was still in Michigan and was one of Dorothy's bridesmaids. Now Rose was twice a mother-in-law. Unlike Alice's faraway marriage, Dorothy lived in Standish, a waitress at Forward's in the always-open restaurant. When their dating got more serious, Elmer brought Dorothy to the farm more than once, but Rose worried. Elmer had continued to drink as he had when he was in the service. He and Vick had clashed more than once over his late nights when Elmer still lived at home, and she had already seen what drink had done to her brother, Vic. But Elmer didn't hide his unfortunate habit from Dorothy when they were engaged, and Rose hoped that, now that he planned on ending his bachelor days, he wouldn't have time for late nights at Red's Bar.

They married at St. Florian's church in Standish after Dorothy had taken instructions and joined the Catholic Church. At least the couple would not have two religions to sort out in their married life. After the wedding mass, the family had a small reception at Dorothy's sister's farmhouse.. Dorothy had been living with her sister and husband, Cleo and Lennie Gulvas.

After his wedding, Elmer looked for a job closer to home than great lakes shipping. Men who worked the boats were away for weeks at a time, and his new wife did not like that. It wasn't a good way to start married life. After a couple of years of rented apartments and working at Forwards' gas pumps, he went to work for

Consumers Power Company as a lineman. At the time, Consumers had a full crew that worked out of Standish. It was the job that he kept until he retired.

Once the couple was established, Elmer bought his Grandma Anna's place. Anna stayed on with Elmer and Dorothy for a few years, rocking their colicky baby, Rosemarie. Elmer tried his hand at part-time farming, and Vick and Rose sent Marylou and Tom to help with hoeing the beans. By now Anna was getting a little slower, but she was still the blunt, fussy woman Rose remembered from her young married days, and Rose knew that her mother-in-law would keep an overly sharp eye on everything that Dorothy did or did not do. Soon enough, Anna took up her old habit of extended visits with Gert and later, with Rose and Vick.

XXXII

We are not sure of sorrow,
And joy was never sure;
Today will die tomorrow;
Time stops for no man's lure;

~ Charles Swinburne

The last three children of the family ended up going to Au Gres, in spite of Vick and Rose's long-held feelings over the consolidation of Hickory Island School. Arlene was already halfway through high school at Arenac Eastern, when Mr. Hoffman, the superintendent of Au Gres, came right to the house and told Vick and Rose they were in Au Gres district, and their kids needed to be in Au Gres School. It was the law. Rose knew it, but she was not happy. The older kids had gone to Standish and to Arenac Eastern and they had been just fine. But this Hoffmann was determined that every student in his district would be in his school. He was cordial and polite and even took the kids for a tour of their new school, but Rose thought him as slippery as a naked snail. Au Gres would get state dollars for her children's attendance. It was all about money, not about which school parents wanted.

Rose's oldest children did not have the same alma mater. Ed and Roseanne graduated from Omer, which went through high school at the time. In 1945, Omer, Turner and Twining were one of the first school consolidations in the state with three cities involved. Omer and Turner became elementary schools only, and the high school for all three schools was located in Twining and christened Arenac Eastern. The high school gym, however, remained at the Omer Community building. The first school buses, originally red, white and blue transported country kids into the town schools, and Lillian and Elmer graduated from Standish during that transition. Alice finished her high school years at the new Arenac Eastern.

Vick and Rose had another homework distraction in their small house the year their youngest three could no longer choose which school bus to ride. Roseanne gave the family a television for Christmas. Although it only got channel 5 in its first years, the family was mesmerized that holiday season with the wonderful box. Marylou and Tom already had an acquaintance with television. Elmer and Dorothy had gotten one the summer before, and the two were allowed to go there once a week and watch it for an hour. When school started after Christmas vacation, Rose once more set rules for use of electronic entertainment, although this time, instead of Vick and his radio, Rose found herself the one tempted. She especially liked the Loretta Young theatre. Even though she turned the volume down low past bedtime hours, she often had to chase Marylou back to bed, who was laying by the upstairs register with her ear glued to the wooden grate.

Arlene seemed to take the move to a new school in stride. She got on the girls' basketball team, got her driver's license, and Vick even let her take the car occasionally, something he never had done with the older kids. She also started dating as soon as she got to the magic age of sixteen and dated every boy in her class. In her senior year, she was not a valedictorian or a salutatorian, but she was prom queen. And her grades were good in the business classes she took. Marylou and Tom started off well, but as they went through junior high, their grades began to fall, and neither seemed especially concerned. Rose asked for homework, and they usually had none. They got it done in study hall.

Meanwhile, after years of working at Fisher Body, Gert and Floyd retired and, as so many who retired from working in the city, decided to live in the country. When Gert asked Vick if they could buy an acre of his farm, he was only too happy to agree. Rose said nothing, but she privately wondered if country life would be all Gert thought it would be. Gert had never learned to drive, and Rose well knew that depending on a ride often meant staying at home. Somehow, Rose couldn't see Gert happy living so far from shops and people and the dozens of other social outlets that city life had to offer. She hadn't been a country gal since her school years in Beaver.

Nevertheless, an acre on the northwestern corner of the farm facing Hale Road was now Gert and Floyd's, and it didn't take long before Vick and Herb Witmer, a neighbor and carpenter by trade, were building a pretty little house on the cleared land. Gert was full of enthusiasm and praise for their work, and Vick's taciturnity melted. Rose could not help but be grateful and a little resentful at the way her sister-in-law changed Vick into the easy, cheerful man that she hadn't seen in years.

XXXIII

These thoughts are depressing I know,...
I wish I was more cheerful, it is more pleasant,
Also it is a duty, we should smile as well as submitting
To the purpose of One Above who is experimenting
With various mixtures of human character which goes best.

~ Stevie Smith

The early summer of 1956 was an eventful one. Arlene graduated from high school, and Ed was installed at Saint Joseph's in Klacking Creek, a small Catholic church outside Rose City. Ed had done his internship as assistant pastor at Visitation in Bay City, and now he would have a parish of his own. Again, she and Vick were the guests of honor when the church greeted their new priest with a huge chicken dinner. The parish hall was full. The people seemed happy to have her son as their new shepherd, and the small country church seemed a perfect fit for Ed. After all, he was a country boy. Even after he had a parish of his own, he still came home every Tuesday for a family visit and put a check under the sugar bowl before he left. He did his best to help the family with his small earnings.

Then one day in the spring of 1958, he had a proposal that was as unexpected as a thunderbolt.

"I need a housekeeper and a caretaker," he said. "The farm isn't going to get you through. You come to work for me and both of you can get a social security number. Think about it."

Rose looked at Vick. He would never agree to such a move. But Father Ed was right. They had to think about their old age. Their savings were small, certainly not enough to live on when they could no longer work, and farmers were not part of the social security plan passed in the Roosevelt years. In the war years and for awhile after, their life had seemed secure, but again the world was changing. Their small farm was gradually becoming obsolete. The small creamery in Standish had closed, and Vick could no longer sell the cream that had been their grocery money for years. Threshing machines had been replaced with combines and horses with tractors. Vick had bought a small Ford tractor in 1947, but it was already ten years old and the tractors and combines continued to grow both in size and price. They didn't have the money to quit and they didn't have the money to stay in.

"What do you think?" Rose asked Vick after Father Ed left.

"I think we should do it. Ed says he needs the help."

Rose was taken by surprise at his fast agreement. "But the farm. What about the cattle? What about the kids?" Tom and Marylou were in their first years of high school.

"I won't sell the farm," Vick said. "We can't live with a priest after we're done working."

"But we can't keep the cattle here."

Vick scratched his head and frowned, but he didn't have an answer. It would not be an easy thing to just get up and move. Their farm might be small, but it was their life investment. Rose had just gotten decent kitchen cupboards and an inside bathroom a few short years ago. Vick had recently cleared a new field and bought a hay loader to shorten the job of harvesting the loose hay that filled the mows every summer. The new strawberry patch had yielded so much fruit they had to sell the fast-ripening berries on a pick-your-own basis.

The following week Father Ed brought up the subject again. A decision would have to be made soon. It was close to planting time.

"It's a big move," Rose started.

"What if you come and work the summer and see how it goes? Marylou and Tom are old enough to take care of the cattle, and Elmer and Dorothy are right next door. Then in the fall, you can start selling off the livestock, and the kids can go to Saint Joe's High School in West Branch."

"I guess we could check on them every week," Rose said. Father Ed had just given his offer an element hard to resist. The kids would be going to a Catholic high school. That would be so much better than Au Gres. Marylou, who had been a good student through grade school, in the past year had brought home report cards that looked almost as bad as Elmer's had been. Rose blamed the school and that study hall arrangement that gave Marylou and Tom that ready excuse. Tom's mediocre report cards were more to the point. He put up with school because he had no other choice.

Gert was bitterly disappointed at Vick and Rose's new venture. "I just move here and you move out!"

"We'll be back to check on things," Rose said.

"It won't be the same."

Rose glanced at Vick. She knew how he felt about his sister, and she knew how he felt about leaving the farm. "We've got to do it, Gert," Rose said. "It's our only chance to get some kind of security when we can't work anymore."

Gert made a face, but she didn't say more. She recognized that they would need a retirement income, and it would be small enough even so.

Even while Rose was adjusting to this new state of affairs she wrestled with another change in the family, Arlene's wedding. Arlene had left home the summer after she graduated and worked in Grand Rapids at a good office job. Her move to Grand Rapids was not a shot in the dark. Roseanne had moved back to Michigan and already had an apartment there. Unlike Roseanne's experience with sharing an apartment with Alice in California, Roseanne and Arlene got along well, and Rose had been happy for her two working daughters.

However, Arlene had stayed in contact with Jake Dewald, a Twining boy, that she had met at the Arenac County fair in her senior year. When Jake left to spend his years in the army, she had continued to write to him, and when he came back home, they continued their relationship and were soon engaged.

Rose objected to the marriage. Jake was a nice enough man, but marrying outside their religion was not right and Jake, unlike Elmer's Dorothy, was not going to adopt the Catholic faith. Arlene figured Jake's religion was his own business and they would marry anyway. Rose saw that her usually mild-mannered daughter was not going to change her mind. Perhaps she and Vick had spoiled this round, happy baby who was the prom queen, who dated every boy in her class, who played on the girls' basketball team. What had this school brought to their family but the first mixed marriage of her children?

Arlene moved back to Arenac County and got a job at the Arenac Independent. In spite of Rose's arguments and Arlene's tears, Jake and Arlene went on with wedding plans. Arlene bought a waltz-length dress and veil, found dresses and hats for Roseanne and Marylou, her maids of honor, ordered flowers, and arranged for the priest at Saint Edward's in Omer to officiate.

Father Ed would not conduct the wedding, nor did he attend, but Rose could not turn her back on Arlene's wedding day. She and the family attended the small wedding in the rectory of Saint Edward's in June of 1958. No big wedding with Rose's daughter walking down the aisle. Jake's groomsmen were Elmer and his one brother, Clarence. Rose made a small supper at the farm house, but none of Jake's family came. Even Clarence had left after the short ceremony. It seems Jake's Baptist family was even more upset about Jake's marriage to a Catholic girl. Rose felt a little bad for her new son-in-law at that point. She couldn't have done such a thing to Arlene. The new couple moved into a house in Au Gres and started their life together and did their best to ignore the religious storm their marriage had caused.

After the wedding, Rose and Vick found themselves working away from home for the first time in their married lives. They applied for social security, the magic numbers that would help them when they couldn't work anymore. It was a far-sighted plan. The church once more, with the help of Father Ed, had come to their rescue.

Floyd died the year they left, and shortly afterwards, Gert sold the pretty little house that Vick was so proud of building and moved back to Flint. The house still stands on the northwestern corner of the Trombley farm. Vick and Herb Witmer had done a good job.

XXXIV

It was as if I had stepped free into space
alone with nothing that I had not
known before.

~ Seamus Heaney

Life at Klacking Creek proved to be another move in Rose's life that had its own set of dilemmas. Leaving Marylou and Tom at the farm that first summer was an interlude that she needed. Rose had a whole new kitchen and house to settle. The rectory was huge and Father Ed had already planned the living space to accommodate them. He gave over the big master bedroom upstairs to the family as their living room, as well as the adjoining bathroom. The back stairs from the kitchen would be their access. The front rooms on the first floor were reserved for parish business—an office, a sitting room and a formal dining room, separated from the cavernous kitchen by a butler's pantry with a cupboard of formal dinnerware that Rose hadn't seen since her days at the Stephanowski's. The kitchen was equipped with more pots and pans than she thought she would ever need, and it alarmed her to think that she would be expected to use the cookware to provide the meals for a priest with a formal dining room. But as the summer went on, Rose found that Father Ed preferred eating in the kitchen the usual meals she had always cooked.

In spite of the elaborate space, she found that keeping house for her priest-son was easier than keeping a farm house with a wood stove, a garden, and messy tracked-in dirt and dust from the barn and fields. She kept the front rooms spotless, and felt guilty that the job was so easy. Even the weekly visits to the farm worked well that summer. Neither Marylou nor Tom could go further than their bikes would take them. The cows looked well cared for and, if Marylou kept house a little messier than Rose would have liked, she kept her thoughts to herself. She well remembered her years when she lived with Vick's mother, and Marylou was younger with less experience. Marylou was as happy describing her ability to fry hamburgers and make strawberry shortcake as if she knew it all (Rose had made sure the freezer had enough strawberries and hamburger to get the two through the summer). Rose realized then how hard it must have been for Anna to see her house cared for by another.

In the fall of 1958, the first clouds on the new arrangement made their appearance when Marylou and Tom moved in September to go to the Catholic high school, Saint Joe's in West Branch. Father Ed had arranged that also. He would teach religion classes to offset tuition charges, and Marylou and Tom could ride with him to school, since his were the first classes of the day, and then come back on the public school bus. Father Ed was not a naturally-gifted teacher, and high school students were a bad audience. Nevertheless, he persevered.

In spite of Father Ed's careful arrangements, two teens in the quiet rectory stirred disruption. They came home from school, hungry, impatient with the set meal time, and clattered up and down the back stairs like a couple of elephants. They also clattered to one another's rooms and shared their record player and listened to music too loud. In spite of the size of the rectory, it certainly wasn't sound proof. Rose needed to keep a harmony between Father Ed, who had tried so hard to accommodate his rectory to two teens, who were not openly subversive, and yet seemed to raise the very dust motes in the air around them.

She tried to keep up with their lives, but somehow the summer when her youngest children had lived apart from her and Vick had opened a divide between their concerns and her's. They argued about Elvis Presley and Pat Boone, they acted as if the news of Buddy Holly's death was a personal tragedy, they admired cars she barely recognized, and they compared their likes and dislikes of the nuns who taught them with no reverence whatsoever.

Marylou, now in her sophomore year, seemed to like the arrangement. She decorated her room with her own pictures, piled it with books and art projects. Her grades soared. Tom, on the other hand, a humble freshman, did not do as well. School was not his favorite place to be, and a nice room of his own and a ride to school in the morning made no impression on him. He wanted the summer on the farm back again.

Oddly enough, Vick seemed oblivious to the discordant energy. He mowed, trimmed, shoveled snow, fixed light sockets or upturned tiles as if he was planting or harvesting a field; he who said he would never move by another man's whistle took up his job as janitor for his priest-son as easily as if he had been born to it. He greeted parishioners affably, he went to church every day, and his quiet seething and violent explosions had disappeared.

Rose found herself isolated from both Vick and her youngest children. Since her work as a housekeeper did not seem to deserve her monthly check, she looked for what else she could do. The church upkeep was hired out to Loretta, a bland-faced woman, who came to the church every week and whisked a broom and dust cloth through the church. She and her widowed mother lived across the road, and the arrangement had gone on long before Father Ed arrived, and Father Ed saw little reason to change it. But Rose saw neglected areas, she saw wax buildup on the floor, and she saw a hundred and one ways that the church should be kept. So she spent her extra time dusting or mopping and eventually, crawling on her knees and removing all the wax build up and rewaxing. It never occurred to her that her work would be Father Ed's first confrontation with his parish.

Loretta and her mother were related to half the people in the small community, and everyone knew that Loretta was limited. They had turned a blind eye to wax build up or anything else that was not well done. Rose may have shined up the church, but Loretta felt displaced and hurt. Rose had put her foot in the middle of a hornet's nest of family alliances that quickly grew out of control. The priest's mother was trying to take over.

"You have to go over and apologize," Father Ed said to Rose. He issued his directive, looking at the salt and pepper shaker in the middle of the table.

"I didn't do anything wrong," Rose protested.

"You hurt Loretta's feelings. That's what you're apologizing for," Father Ed said.

Rose was humiliated. She was ordered by her boss, her own son, to do something she felt she did not have to apologize for. She didn't say more. Vick continued eating fried potatoes and sauerkraut as if he hadn't heard a thing.

In spite of her stuttering apology the next day, Father Ed had been right. Loretta and her mother agreed that Rose's intrusive gestures were not meant to topple Loretta from her job as church caretaker and if Rose wanted to dust and polish on her own time, all was okay. Rose had done what had to be done, but life had changed. What she did, what the family did, could help or hurt Father Ed. They lived in a fishbowl.

In the next years, Rose worried about family intrusion. They took Anna for the summer, in spite of the fact that she was an extra family member that might be looked upon as an expense to the parish, one more thing that could rise up against them. Father Ed did not see his grandmother's 'visit' in the same way, and Father Ed was right. Although Vick's mother stirred no waves in the parish, Anna felt much like Tom did. She wanted to be back at the farm that now stood abandoned.

Anna was at Klacking Creek when Gert married again. After Floyd's death and Gert's move back to Flint, her life had not been one of a tragic widow. She let it be known that she wanted a man in her life and she found Art Hertier, who had been in love with her years before. When he went off to war (World War I), Gert had chosen Floyd Kingsland instead. Art was a kind, gentle man, who had lost his wife and wanted companionship as much as Gert did. Rose liked Art far more than she had ever liked the hard--drinking, flamboyant Floyd. Gert's second marriage was like something out of a fairy tale when the good guy finally wins.

Gert had held Rose on her lap to get her to the hospital to ensure that Ed would be born. Now he who would seal her marriage. Tom would be the altar boy, and Marylou would sing the mass. Rose worried about that. Father Ed had paid for Marylou to take lessons so she could play the organ for his high masses. Was she ready to sing a wedding mass? But the wedding went off without a flaw. Gert got it right. They went to Iva's Chcken Dinners for the wedding reception, and Rose didn't have to do a thing.

Rose welcomed the next marriage at Klacking Creek even more. Roseanne married Bob Bush in August of 1959. After Elmer and Alice and Arlene's weddings, Roseanne worried that she would never marry. Her family, her friends, everyone she knew fell in love and married as easily as spring. Roseanne had met Bob in California while he was there visiting friends and, as shy as Roseanne could be, they were drawn together and dated before he had to go back to Grand Rapids. He was a fulltime fireman, a Catholic, and he left every hint that he would like to know her better. Roseanne, already tired of California, followed him to Michigan and got a job in Grand Rapids. They dated more seriously. Then his widowed mother intervened. Bob was her only son, and she would not tolerate another woman taking her place in her son's life. Bob could not deal with his mother's consternation and broke off their relationship.

Roseanne was devastated. She had made a fool of herself chasing him to Grand Rapids like a lovestruck school girl, and she was nearing thirty. But a few months later, his mother died of the heart attack she had threatened and, after a decent interval, Bob was back and Roseanne was glad she had kept her anger and disappointment to herself.

"She's waited long enough, but she can still have babies," Anna said to Rose.

"A marriage needs babies," Rose agreed.

Again, Father Ed officiated, Marylou sang, and Tom was altar boy. The family was trying to carry on as if the rectory was the new homestead, but it wasn't. It was Father Ed's job, and the rectory belonged to the parish. Vick and Rose were employees and Rose worried with every family event that they were intruding on Fr. Ed's time as a parish priest.

XXXV

the children will not repeat
the phrases their parents speak
somebody has persuaded them
that it is better to say everything differently
so that they can be admired somewhere
farther and farther away...

~ W.S. Merwin

A year after they moved, Vick and Rose reluctantly rented the farmhouse to Dorothy's youngest sister, Carol, and her husband, Joe Trombley, who was not related to Vick, as far as they knew. The Trombley name had spread far and wide since those first Trombley brothers had settled in Bay County in the 1800's, and there were three distinct Trombley families in Standish, who did not know when and where they had ever been related.

At any rate, Rose thought it better that somebody live there than nobody at all, and soon enough, Carol invited Marylou and Tom to stay there anytime they wanted. Tom promptly went for the whole summer to help Elmer with the crops he tried to farm. Marylou, without such an excuse, went and stayed for some of the summer anyway. Rose did not like the whole arrangement. Carol and Joe were much too young to watch two teens. Vick had no objections, and Rose almost wished for his thunderous explosion for the very idea.

Unfortunately, Vick sold their 1949 Chevy to the two. Marylou had her driver's license, she had an income from playing organ for the church as well as a part time job as a waitress in West Branch, but Tom knew how to change the oil, change a tire and listen to an engine. The car would be a joint project, and Rose suspected that Tom would likely drive even though he didn't have his license yet. They immediately painted the gray-green car black. Rose watched them with their dark paint and wide brushes and wondered why the car had to be black. They lived in a different world than anything she knew.

That year the teen pressure cooker erupted. The school year opened and Marylou and Tom did not ride with Father Ed anymore. They drove the black Chevy to school, and Marylou talked about Dale Bugh that she had met at Eastman's pit that summer. She decided she would see him whenever possible. Once he even hitch-hiked to the rectory. He was young and shy and he didn't even have a car of his own. When Rose tried to warn Marylou about dating someone outside the church, Marylou only said, "Mom, you talk too much." That hurt. Why couldn't Marylou see that this was more than her right to date whomever she wanted? Didn't Father Ed's parish count?

In October, the 49 Chevy was upside down in the Pine River less than two miles from Dale Bugh's house. Tom and Marylou were supposed to be in West Branch at a football game. Tom was driving and the car skidded on the loose gravel around one of the curves. Fortunately no one was hurt, but the car was wrecked.

In spite of the accident, which should have been a wakeup call, Marylou asserted her right to date whomever she wanted. Rose was astounded. Marylou might be a senior, but this was too much. Rose was having no more daughters dating non-Catholic boys, especially now that they were living in a priest's rectory.

After a pitched battle with her stubborn daughter, Marylou got on a bus in West Branch and left home. In spite of Vick and

Rose's pleas, Marylou did not go back to school. She got a job in Standish and later in Bentley. Vick was little support. He had driven to Standish when they knew where Marylou had gone, but all he said when she refused to come home was, "Lord help you, girl."

That spring Marylou told Rose she had to get married. She was pregnant. Rose was shocked. Her own daughter a girl in trouble like Amelia Klinsky. She remembered Mrs. Stephanowski's words those years ago: "Someday my girls might need help."

"You don't *have* to get married," she told Marylou. "I can help you with the baby."

"Dale said it's his baby too, and he wants to be the father," Marylou said. "It'll work out."

Rose didn't know Dale well, except that he was one of Mabel Lentz's grandchildren, but Marylou and Dale were teens and high-school dropouts. It wasn't like it had been when people married young in Rose's day. High school was no longer a possibility for some, but a necessity for all. Her youngest daughter was starting a marriage with everything against it. Nevertheless, Marylou and Dale married in June of 1960 in a rectory in Swartz Creek with no one attending, except for two witnesses that the priest had arranged to appear and sign the legal documents.

Tom finished high school in 1961, the year after Marylou left, although he too left the rectory and St. Joe's high school before he graduated. Carol and Joe had moved out of the farm house after their first-born died a crib death and Carol could no longer stay there. Tom decided he could do just fine living back at the farm and finishing high school in AuGres. Again, Rose argued, but this time her arguments were weak. Even Father Ed did not back her as he had when Marylou asserted her right to make her own choices, as bad as that had turned out. Would Tom leave and not graduate at all? Her last three children had insisted on choices, clearly against their parents' wishes. Against her better judgment, she let Tom do as he wanted, and Tom finished high school living on the farm by himself. He enlisted in the army before he was drafted. It was a strange piece of luck. Tom served in Korea, but the war was over and he came home before he had to fire a shot.

Meanwhile, Alice's stormy marriage fell apart much as Roseanne predicted it would. Catholics didn't divorce—Rose knew very few that even lived apart as Anna had chosen to do with John Holka. But in California, evidently Catholics divorced, although as time went on, it seemed Alice's disputes with the father of her two children were almost as bitter as their marriage had been.

The family was being rocked by the waves of the new world that inserted itself into their lives. Rock and roll, TV, young people with their own cars; As the sixties rolled on, Rose watched the news as the country mourned the assassination of President Kennedy, as freedom marches erupted across the South, as young people thronged streets and campuses and demanded their government pass Civil Right laws and withdraw troops from Viet Nam. Rose had to agree with some of it, but the dress, the dances, the flagrant disobedience to policemen alarmed her. Never had she seen such widespread disrespect for authority. It seemed the country was falling apart and pulling away from all Rose held sacred.

Whatever misgivings Rose had, she was soon taken up with a whole new generation of babies born into this changing world. Elmer and Dorothy had already started their family that continued to grow until they had nine children. Now the latest marriages brought several more grandchildren into her and Vick's lives within a few years of each other. Arlene had three boys, Marylou had three boys and a girl, and Roseanne had two sons. Except for Alice's babies,

Rose made time away from her housekeeping duties to help with all of them.

Tom, however, came home after he served in Korea and settled into bachelorhood on the farm where he grew up. He was uncle to many and father to none, and didn't seem to feel any need to change his single way of life.

XXXVI

I am tired of tears and laughter,
And those that laugh and weep;
Of what may come hereafter
For all that sow to reap:

~ Charles Swinburne

Rose hung up the phone in Father Ed's office. Her eyes passed over the room looking for dust. The rectory was so big that Rose had to keep a vigilant eye for missed corners. She could only wonder at the huge rectories that the church put up for single priests. Heating alone must cost a fortune. She touched the African violet in the northern window, a thing of beauty in full bloom. She had never had a houseplant like that at the farm. Her house plants there were sturdy cactuses or 'Irish Roses', plants that needed little attention.

She went through the dining room, only used when Father Ed entertained other priests. The large table was covered with a crocheted table cloth that Aunt Gert had made, another point of pride, not something that their farm table ever had. Rose remembered Bishop Wosniscieki's visit that put her in a panic. Rose had no idea what a bishop ate and Father Ed was no help. He didn't know how to boil water. That was why he had his mother in the kitchen. But after dinner the bishop came to the kitchen and warmly complimented her on the meal. It seems the Polish bishop thought steak with mushrooms was as good as manna from Heaven.

When she got to the kitchen, Vick stood by the sink with a tall glass of water he had just drawn. "Ma's worse again," Rose said. Calling Anna 'Ma' had always come easy to Rose, since her own

Anna Trombley on her Hickory Island farm

mother had always been Mama and her stepmother had always been Stepmother.

Vick mopped the sweat off his face with his red work handkerchief. "I've got the grass mowed. We'd better go."

Rose checked the refrigerator. There were enough leftovers for Father Ed's supper. They had been taking so much time away since Anna had started to fail. But, in spite of Rose's concerns, Father Ed was an easy employer when it came to matters of family.

Anna had several good years after she moved to Hickory Island. She had made a quilt for each of her grandchildren, and the huge quilting loom that she set up in her parlor took up half the room. She also planted flower gardens all around the house, wallpapered her outhouse, and raised a vegetable garden every summer. The only thing she never did on her Hickory Island acres was farm.

But life had changed for Anna in the last years. She had stayed with Rose and Vick on and off since she had sold her place to Elmer, alternating between Gert during the winter months and Rose and Vick's farm in the summer. She never wanted to stay at Father Ed's rectory. Rose smiled a little when she remembered that Anna had planted a small flower garden at the farm only three years ago. She wanted to plant her flowers, and the rectory lawn didn't work.

As she and Vick drove to the Sterling Nursing Home, Rose thought of the last years that had led to this July day in 1966. At first, when Anna insisted on staying on the farm, she stayed by herself, and Rose and Vick came to the farm on their time off, but as Anna got older and more fragile, Rose hired Marylou to stay with her Grandma during the week and also gave her the job of ironing the church linen; fussy, time-consuming work that Marylou did surprisingly well.

Rose hurt for her stubborn daughter that year, who was still a big kid and already showing with the baby she would have. As Rose had foreseen, the young couple's life bordered on catastrophe. They lived in a trailer where the old Hickory Island School had been after Dale had worked for a farmer in Swartz Creek who went broke and could not pay him for over a hundred hours that he owed the destitute couple. Dale's dad had towed their small trailer to his back yard, but that wasn't right, so Rose offered them the acre to park the trailer. At least they could hook the toilet into the old septic tank that still existed from the school days, although they had no running water and hauled water from Vick and Rose's, and Dale did not have a job.

The following summer, Marylou and Dale were gone from the Hickory Island acre. With a lot of help from Dale's dad and a donation from Anna, the couple had put up a house on an acre of Dale's dad's Kraushaar Road farm. After the move, Marylou had no transportation but still, Rose and Vick managed to keep Anna where she was the happiest. Tom was back from the service and living at the farm. It wasn't like having a woman with Anna, but at least it was someone in the house.

The day Anna could no longer stay there was as clear as if it had happened yesterday, although it was a year ago. Anna came out of the front bedroom to go to the bathroom, as she did every morning and fell by the kitchen cupboard. For no reason, she fell.

Tom worked nights at Northern Tube in Pinconning and had not yet gone to work and, luckily, Vick and Rose were also there that day. Together Tom and Rose lifted her. "I've got to go to the toilet," Anna said. Tom fetched a galvanized pail and she went, squatted there on the pail in the middle of the kitchen.

"Please don't send me away," she said to Rose.

Rose's heart turned over. How humiliating it must be to sit on a pail in front of people and go to the toilet.

"Right now, let's just get you in bed," Rose said, and breathed a silent prayer of thanksgiving that Tom was there to help her.

Anna stayed in bed all day without complaint, and Rose almost began to believe that no harm had been done when the pain started. Rose called the ambulance late that evening, and her worst fears were true. Anna had broken her hip, and she wouldn't walk again. They had to put her in a nursing home that, to Anna, was worse than death.

When Vick and Rose arrived at the nursing home, Anna was conscious. "They're killing me," she whispered. "Pills, pills, pills. The pills are killing me."

On one of Rose and Vick's visits, Rose had offered to pray with Anna and she had flung her rosary across the room. "I prayed all my life so I can die in peace, and what do they send me!" she fumed. "A Protestant minister!"

"Ma!" Rose protested, "That was Father LaBorie. He's been at the French catholic church in Standish for fifty years."

"Well, he sounded like a Protestant," Anna insisted. Rose had to smile. The priest's heavy French accent didn't have anything to do with his theology, but Rose didn't argue. Anna still had a streak of the stubborn will that had kept her going all these years.

Now Rose again offered to pray with her. This time Anna gripped Rose's hand, her own frail and shaking. Rose sat by her bed and read a prayer for the dying, and Anna's hand relaxed and her eyes closed at the words of comfort.

"Don't let me die alone," she murmured when Rose finished.

Rose looked at Vick standing by the foot of the bed. He took the other chair in the small room. The summer sun crept across the sky and the hours lengthened as the long day deepened into evening. Anna spoke little, her blue-veined eyes closed, her small figure withered on the white pillow.

A nurse tiptoed in and beckoned them into the hall. "She may hang on like this for a long time," she whispered. "You've been here all day. Go home and get some rest. I'll call you if she worsens even a little."

They drove back to Klacking Creek, too numb with tiredness to even conjecture how long Anna could go on. Before they even got to bed, the nurse called as she had promised. By the time they got back to Sterling, Anna had died– alone.

Now Rose felt truly orphaned. Anna was her and Vick's last link with the generation that had been the 'elders'. Rose's Tata had died before her youngest children had more than a few memories of the man that had shaped her young life. Stepmother followed a few years after Tata, as fearful of the growing cancer that consumed her as she had been about her first pregnancies. Rose had even taken Stepmother for awhile to give Leo and Virginia a break and tried to care for her, but Stepmother only wanted to go back to her home before the end. Everyone at the end only wanted to be home.

Anna had probably never thought of the end of her life in those terms. She told the family more than once that she did not want any bawling at her funeral. She wanted them dancing on her casket, and she was going to be in a better place to be sure they did it. And, after 96 years on earth, Anna was ready for a change of scene.

Gert's fund of family jokes and stories after the funeral was as inexhaustible as ever, and she had the whole family laughing at the good old days. But Rose's smile was tinged with a sad guilt. She could still see the tiny withered figure against the stark white of the hospital bedding and hear her whisper, "Don't let me die alone."

Rose looked at Vick and Gert raising a beer to toast their mother's long life. Vick was already 72 and Rose was 65. They would be next, she thought, and a chill shook her in spite of the warm July afternoon.

The chill deepened the next year when Sterling Nursing Home was closed for improper practices. Anna had not been out of her mind when she complained to them, "Pills, pills, pills." The place had been over-sedating their patients to keep them in bed.

Vick and Rose on their 50th wedding anniversary

XXXVII

The bitter apple and the bite in the apple.
And the ragged rock in the restless waters,
Waves wash over it, fogs conceal it;...
but in the somber season
Or the sudden fury, is what it always was

~ T.S. Eliot

In 1970 Vick and Rose came back to the farm to stay. Two years earlier, Father Ed was sent to Gladwin, and Vick and Rose moved with him, but the new parish was not Klacking Creek, and neither one of them felt they could do the work they once did. They could collect social security in their last years. For Rose, the return home was a long sigh of relief. Their years of traveling back and forth between the farm and the rectory were over.

In September of 1972 she and Vick celebrated their 50th wedding anniversary. Neither wanted a celebration, but the family insisted. Rose felt the same guilt that she had felt at Ed's ordination. Fifty years of a marriage that had been fraught with periods of dissension was not an ideal marriage, but everyone acted as if she and Vick had done something special. They ate dinner at Iva's Chicken Dinners in Sterling, a restaurant that had been in existence almost as long as their marriage. Then the family came back to the farm for a lawn party with a beer keg and a wedding cake. Every one of the kids was there as well as every grandchild. She and Vick cut the cake and kissed, and everyone cheered and toasted another fifty years.

Rose looked at the face of the man with whom she had spent most of the years of her life. While she had always planned and looked forward to things being different, they had lived their lives, raised their children, and aged into two people that had somehow stayed together in a world that kept changing around them. The old neighbors were gone; Uncle Frank, Aunt Tillie, Uncle Walter, Mabel Lentz, Ed Payne—so many.

The next generation had taken over many of the small Hickory Island farms but most, like Elmer, had to work away from home, and many put their land in the land bank, a strange program where the federal government paid farmers not to farm. Julian Nowak, the youngest of Uncle Frank's children, still a bachelor, lived on Uncle Frank's farm and hadn't bowed to the insane arrangement, as Rose thought of it, but struggled to keep his dad's farm together.

She looked at the faces of her grown children and her grandchildren, so different, their attitudes ranging from conservative to liberal. Sooner or later at every family gathering, their ardent political arguments erupted and, as often as not, Rose joined the arguments. Vick did not. He still did not communicate well, but his explosive temper had disappeared. Somehow they had kept the feeling of the family they were.

Gert clapped Rose on the shoulder. "Don't you be making eyes like that at Vick. Next thing you know, you'll be starting another family."

Everyone laughed and Gert helped Rose serve the cake. "You two are retired," Gert said. "It's a big country. Go and see it."

Gert and Art had lured them to Hartwick Pines and the Soo Locks, but Vick was not about to get on a plane and go any further. He was not a traveler. "If I see some of Michigan, that's enough," he said. As usual, she and Vick disagreed. Rose had already gone to California again with Marylou to visit Alice. A whole world was just one step away from getting on a plane.

And so Rose and Vick's second fifty years started. The following May of 1973 dawned much as the others in their retired life. Vick got up and fixed toast and coffee, something he had never done in their younger years. Both the toast and the coffee were black enough to use for shoeshine, but Rose's nagging over such details had faded. Some things in Vick would never change.

They sat down across the table from each other, the small table littered with toast crumbs, a cozy reminder to Rose that she was home and that their days were their own. Right now, Vick was probably planning which brush pile to burn or which fence to fix, and she was going to repot her house plants and open up the sun porch that had been closed all winter to the cold.

She looked out the window and to her surprise, saw Elmer's car drive up to the edge of the lawn and he and Arlene got out. They stood by the car for a minute looking toward the house.

"Why are those two here at this time of the day?" she said aloud.

Vick peered out the window and shrugged.

Rose's uneasiness grew into dread when they came into the kitchen. Both of their faces were sober, and Arlene's eyes were red from crying.

"What's wrong?" Rose asked.

Arlene glanced at Elmer, and his eyes shifted away. "It's Roseanne," Arlene blurted. "She killed herself last night."

The room dimmed and spun, the coziness gone. The talk, the talk, the talk. Arlene told the little bit she knew. Elmer said nothing. Bob had come home from his night shift as a fireman and found Roseanne in the car in the garage with the motor running. Their boys were still asleep. Bob was distraught to Elmer on the phone. No suicide note, she had a birthday card picked out for Arlene's birthday, she had cut out patterns for the boys' summer pajamas. Why? Why? Why?

Rose didn't remember much of that day. How could she bear to bury another daughter, the worst pain, worse than failed love, worse than childbirth, worse than any pain in her life? What did Mike and Pat, Roseanne's two children know? They were already twelve and ten, not that much older than Rose had been when she lost her mother. What horrible impulse had caused Roseanne to abandon the babies she had looked forward to for so long?

Somehow Rose must have looked like she had accepted the devastating news. Somehow, they must have made some kind of plan. When Elmer and Arlene finally left, she couldn't move. She sat staring at the spot where Elmer's car had been. Her oldest daughter, the one who raised a chick behind the kitchen stove and cried when Vick had killed it for Sunday dinner, the one who sewed pajamas and knitted mittens for the younger ones and arrived every Christmas, her car filled with gifts tagged 'from Santa Claus', the one who helped organize their family reunions, the caring, responsible girl. What had gone wrong?

She looked at Vick. He sat there, tears silently falling down his weathered face.

Roseanne was buried in Grand Rapids in the Catholic cemetery. Rose took a small comfort in that. Once, suicides were not given a Catholic burial, but Roseanne and Bob had both been active members in their church. The catastrophe to what had seemed to be the perfect American family, deserved some Christian compassion, or the church realized that suicide was a desperate attempt of a tortured mind and not necessarily an act that deliberately turned away from grace .

Rose did not want to remember that Roseanne had once gotten hooked on prescription drugs and had gone into detox in Knoxville, Tennessee. She had come back from those weeks, sober and serious and married Bob, had her two boys and worked part–time after they were older.

Rose did not want to remember when she had stayed at Bob and Roseanne's just months before. Roseanne had excruciating pain in her shoulder and back and needed help with her boys. After Rose had stayed a week, Roseanne said she felt much better and brought her home.

Now Rose was haunted by the night Roseanne showed her a bottle of prescription pain killers and said, "These will be the death of me." Rose thought she meant the pain. She should have seen that it was the drugs. Roseanne had chosen to die rather than go through addiction again.

XXXVIII

I am a reaper whose muscles set at sundown.
All my oats are cradled
But I am too chilled and too fatigued to bind them.

~ Jean Toomer

In spite of the family tragedy, Tom and Nancy were married in the fall of 1973. Nancy Holmberg worked with Marylou. After her precipitous marriage, Marylou had finished high school, gone on to the recently-opened Saginaw Valley College and earned a teaching certificate and now worked for Pinconning Schools, and Dale now had a secure job at Dobson's in Bay City. Somehow, they had seemed to beat the odds with a lot of family help. Even Vick had altered his feelings at Marylou's unlikely marriage and had given Marylou his Corvair for a dollar, so she had transportation for her last classes (All of Vick's cars after the 1949 Chevy were Father Ed's used vehicles). Rose could only wonder how Vick had changed since their early years. This was the man who didn't think the older kids needed to go to high school.

At any rate, Nancy, a Detroit girl and a newly-hired teacher, had been a Dominican nun, who had left the order the year before and was now boarding at Mary Ellery's, the superintendent's secretary. The church had certainly changed. Men and women got dispensations from their vows as easily as Alice and Joe had divorced. What had happened to commitment through better or worse? Marylou had no such attitude toward such changes. She arranged a date between Tom and Nancy, although later, Marylou told Rose that it never occurred to her that she had just insured herself a new sister-in-law. Tom and Nancy continued to date.

But, as in many love stories, there had been a crisis point. Tom had come back from the army drinking as heavily as Elmer, and a drinking man did not make a good husband. One time he got as drunk as he usually did when he wasn't working and before he was dating Nancy. When he showed up at her door, they didn't go out that evening, and Tom came home after showing Nancy the side of him he had kept away from her. Mary Ellery had not been impressed with Nancy's date either. They would probably never see each other again.

Rose watched her youngest son's remorse at making a fool of himself. It was obvious he really cared for this woman, something she hadn't seen in her youngest son before. She finally said, "Pick up the phone and call her. You showed her the worse you can be. You don't have to be that way if you really care for her."

Oddly enough, her stubborn son did as Rose said and, even more oddly, Nancy agreed to another date. As it turned out, although Tom still drank, his drinking abated and their marriage lasted. Gert came to the wedding with her usual supply of jokes. In spite of Gert's ribald nudging about people marrying in their thirties, Tom and Nancy's five children would arrive about the same time as some of the family's next generation. Bob and his sons also came to the wedding. Although Rose was happy for this new daughter-in-law, she ached for the missing daughter that would never again be part of the family celebrations, and she could only guess how hard the big Polish wedding at Standish's VFW Hall must have been for Bob.

After the wedding, Vick and Rose sold the Hickory Island school lot to Tom. Rose remembered the legal wrangling over the property when the school was consolidated, and she didn't want the farm torn apart by any more court battles. It was time their affairs were put in order. After Tom built his home on the acre lot, they sold him the farm. Rose then arranged prepaid funerals for both herself and Vick, and Tom's farm's payments went into separate accounts for their other kids. Their total income was less than $5000 a year, but they were okay.

Vick wanted the farm to stay in the family, although a separate account for the family and the prepaid funeral were legal maneuvers he distrusted. Once, in their younger years, he had roared at Rose, "You and your damn books!" But this time he did not argue, and Rose knew that part of his failure to object were the increasing headaches that had plagued him for much of his life. He followed the pattern of his years of farming. He still awoke at milking time and went to bed early. Even as he got slower, he mowed grass and mended fences.

Rose could see that his efforts tired him. "Why are you doing all that?" she scolded. "Tom is a young man. He can do it." She may as well have been talking to the wind. They had a life lease on the farm and the farm was still his.

The summer of 1974 Vick and Tom were fixing fences at the back of the farm. On the way back to the house, Vick waved Tom and the tractor away and followed the fence on foot. Tom looked back and saw that his dad had slowed and then stopped. He went back and helped Vick up on the tractor. Vick leaned against the tractor fender, his face white and sweating. "I don't think I'll be walking back here again," he said.

"Why are trying to do all that?" Rose scolded yet again. "You need to see a doctor. You're eating aspirin like candy."

"I'm not going to no damn doctor," he said. "They always find something. Just leave me alone."

The following January, Vick went up to bed early as he usually did. Rose opened the *Bay City Times* and listened to hear the familiar thump of his knees hitting the floor when he knelt down to his prayers. He couldn't bend his knees well, but he fell on them every morning and every night. She had told him more than once that his prayers would be as good if he couldn't kneel, but Vick, as usual, didn't listen to her. He knelt when he prayed.

The house fell silent except for the rustling of the paper and the snap of the wood fire in the kitchen stove. The evening slid by until Rose's eyes burned with fatigue, and she saw that it was close to midnight.

Suddenly, she heard a thump and a strangled noise, and she rushed upstairs. Vick lay on the floor unable to move.

"Jasne kochany!" Rose cried. She put a pillow under his head and put down a cloth where he had thrown up. "I'm going to call Tom." Vick tried to reply and Rose saw that he couldn't talk either. Mercifully, they now had a phone that the kids insisted they have. Vick never used the thing, but tonight she thanked God and the family that it was there.

She ran downstairs and called Tom's number.

"Tom's in the shower," Nancy answered. "He'll be right over."

"Should I call the ambulance?"

"Go back to him. Tom's on his way."

A click on the line told them that the party line was alive and well. Any neighbor's call rang in their phone, although every ring was different. Dorothy knew Vick and Rose's ring, and she knew Tom's ring. Neither called one another at midnight. Dorothy picked up the phone and listened in. She called an ambulance and then sent her two boys with lanterns to stand by the driveway, so it wouldn't miss the place. She was in Rose's kitchen when the ambulance crew arrived and maneuvered the narrow stairs and carried Vick down on a stretcher.

"He doesn't want to go to a hospital," Tom protested. "He wants to stay here."

"He's had a stroke," Dorothy said. "He's got to go to a hospital right now– at least for awhile. We'll follow them."

Anna's words came back to Rose. "Don't send me away." But she had to agree with Dorothy. They couldn't just leave Vick on the floor.

"We'll be with him," Dorothy said. "Don't worry, Ma. We'll be with him."

Marylou got a call from Dorothy and got to Standish hospital at two in the morning. Tom had already taken Rose home. Dorothy had insisted that the emergency doctor was right. Vick would get tests and it would take hours. Rose needed to rest and the hospital was no place to rest. As Dorothy promised, the family would be with him. Marylou and Dorothy stayed the night.

For a brief time the next morning, Vick seemed to rally. Although he couldn't talk, he understood when Dorothy fed him oatmeal and coffee. "You've got to have your coffee, Pa," she said. Vick tried to smile and nodded his head.

Shortly after that one lucid moment, Vick lapsed into a coma. The family, one at a time, gathered at the hospital. When Rose came back, Doctor Casten told Rose it was a massive stroke.

The family did not take the news well. Although Vick had always had headaches, and Rose knew that they had been worse lately, he could and would recover as he always had. "He could be like this for a long time before he comes around," Rose said. "I hope he doesn't have to stay in a wheelchair. He would hate that."

Gert arrived late that afternoon. Rose didn't even remember who called her. It must have been Dorothy. "Oh my god, my god, he's dying!" Gert cried when she came into the room.

Rose was surprised at her reaction. She hurried her out into the hall. "The nurses tell us that he might hear," she said. "Don't be saying things like that."

"He's dying," Gert said again, and her sobs echoed down the shiny hall. "Does Father Ed know?"

"He went to the Holy Land," Rose objected. "He's been planning this trip for weeks. Vick can be like this for days. Father Ed doesn't need to come back right now."

"He's coming back, Ma," Dorothy said. "He's on his way." Somehow, Dorothy had traced him and told him to come back home.

Rose looked at the faces of her family who had followed them into the hall. Father Ed wouldn't be cutting back his first and only trip to the Holy Land unless Gert was right.

As the evening deepened, Gert whispered, "Let's go pray." The family followed her into an empty waiting room, and they knelt by the shiny plastic couches and prayed, the chant of the Rosary filling the sterile space. When the last 'Hail Mary' floated through the air, they went back to Vick's bed, children, grandchildren, Gert, Rose. Gert's suggestion for prayer was a good idea, Rose thought. Vick could still come around on the wings of their prayers.

Marlene Sivic was at Vick's bedside. Once she hoed beans in her dad's field with Tom and Marylou. It seemed incongruous that this young kid knew to put a cool cloth on Vick's forehead and feel his legs for the first signs of death. "He's going," she said briefly. How could anyone so young wear a nurse's uniform and know about death? Rose watched Vick's stillness, heard the last small sigh of breath as Marlene checked once more for the pulse that was no longer there.

Father Ed didn't get home in time to be with the family when Vick died, but he got home to say the mass and deliver the eulogy that sent his father to Heaven.

XXXIX

The stars are not wanted now: put out every one;
Pack up the moon and dismantle the sun;
Pour away the ocean and sweep up the wood;
For nothing now can ever come to any good.

~ W.H. Auden

Seven years passed. Rose was now eighty-three, but it seemed strange to hear her age. Inside, she felt like a young woman, and when she bothered to look into a mirror to adjust a collar, she almost smiled at how different she looked from how she felt. The summer after Vick's death, she went to Mexico and Hawaii with Father Ed. She went to California with Marylou to visit Alice. That was the year Alice and Marylou convinced her to quit trying to bottle dye her hair and get the first real hair style she had since the day when Gert had lured her into getting a bob in the twenties. She found in the months following that her waved, white hair was actually kind of attractive. She watched Tom's five children grow, and even babysat when Nancy had to go to town. The latest grandchildren made a path across the field from their place to hers and filled her days with their young energy.

Marylou and Dale divorced after twenty-three years of a volatile marriage. And Arlene, who had fussed over her dad, now fussed over Rose. The house that Vick had fixed up before they would get their new one in five years was still standing and she was still living in it. She felt like she had reached a peaceful plateau, and she now had the time to read and listen to her grandchildren, things life had always rushed her through. She felt content. She thought that she had seen the worst that life could give.

It was a hot day in July when Nancy came across the field. "Jake called," she said as soon as she came through the door. "Arlene's at St. Mary's in Saginaw."

Rose couldn't grasp this news. "They just left for their vacation week at Houghton Lake," she said. "How could she be in Saginaw?"

Nancy hesitated. "She had this terrible headache. They're doing some tests. We're trying to get hold of Marylou. She must not have the phone connected in her new place yet."

Rose felt a chill of fear. Why call Marylou about some tests? Something was very wrong. "When you get her, tell her I want to go to the hospital with her," Rose ordered. This was more than a terrible headache.

By the next day, the tests confirmed a brain tumor, but Arlene had Doctor Fields, the best neurosurgeon in the state. The man could work miracles, and he wasn't waiting. He scheduled surgery for the next day. Everything was happening too fast. The next day Rose and Marylou came to the hospital to sit with Jake and Arlene's three sons. Rod, the oldest, found reasons to get up and walk out of the room. Bobby sat as if hypnotized into silence and young Ronnie, still in middle school, fidgeted and paced like a young, caged animal. Rose and Jake flipped through magazines and Marylou fitfully poured one more cup of bad coffee from the giant coffee urn that stood in the corner of the waiting room.

Minutes stretched into hours. They tried to talk about the weather, the news that flickered on the TV, the time that led up to this minute. The equal rights amendment that had failed to pass by three states held no interest for Rose today, nor for any of them, not even Marylou. Rose tried to pray, and her silent words sent to God were disjointed fragments. Please. Help her, God, Mother Mary. Please.

When Doctor Fields finally came into the room, they all stood as if pulled up by strings. The surgery had gone well. He had removed the tumor completely without damage. The tumor was malignant. The malignant cells had traveled from elsewhere in her body.

Jake asked a few questions, little things about recovery. They listened and nodded as if they were talking about an appendectomy. Malignant cells screamed at Rose. She turned abruptly. Like a wounded animal, she sought refuge, away from the waiting room, away from her son-in-law, away from her grandsons, whose faces had turned to stone. Rose knew they had to do that; she knew how to do that herself. But this time she couldn't stop the tears. She didn't need to ask the bigger questions. She already knew the answers. She escaped to the restroom around the corner.

She fled blindly into one of the stalls. When she came out, Marylou was standing there, tears running down her face. They held one another, the humming silence of the room broken only by a sob or a ragged breath. Malignant cells. Cancer. The unsaid word hung over them. More tests. Perhaps the malignancy had been caught in time. They had to hold on to those slivers of hope.

Alice somehow scraped up the money for plane fare and came from California by herself that summer. Her children, Jim and Sue, were already young adults away from home and trying to survive on their own. The family decided to go ahead with a family reunion, although this year, it was at Marylou's. After her divorce, she had moved into a place on Senske Road, bought a month before. She told Rose a family reunion was a perfect time to introduce her new home to the family, but they both knew that Rose could not plan for a family reunion on the farm this year.

At the reunion, Arlene still wore a headband over the surgery scar, but otherwise, belied the shock and tears of that day on the fourth floor of Saint Mary's.

"The headache's gone," she said. "The only thing Doctor Fields removed I don't like is the phone directory I kept in my head." She was a secretary at Au Gres High School and her phone directory was important to her.

"It'll come back," Jake reassured her.

"What do I know?' Marylou said. "I can't remember my new phone number. That's why they have phone directories and post it notes."

The family laughed. Marylou was a number illiterate.

Marylou's youngest, Jim, still living with her, had a pet raccoon that he brought out and posed on the beer keg. Rose had never seen a coon treated like a pet, and the little masked critter looked as cute as a big kitty, but Jim warned everyone to look and not touch. Evidently, he was not as mellow as a big kitty. Marylou said, "Prohibition would have worked if they had enlisted help from "Cooner" and his buddies to guard the beer kegs."

Rose was happy that the reunion's change of setting went well, even though it was smaller than usual. Roseanne's Bob and boys couldn't be there, but Elmer and most of his family came, as well as Jake and Arlene and their boys and Marylou's kids. In spite of the attempts at matching Arlene's optimism, they all knew that she would fight her diagnosis with everything she had. She wanted to see her youngest son, Ron, graduate, and she would jump every medical hoop to get there. Rose knew the odds, and so did Alice and Marylou. Alice's son, Jim, in training to be a pharmacist, bluntly told Alice that the only good news was that Arlene knew how she was going to go. They don't know everything, Rose thought. There was hope and prayer.

The following week, Rose went with her daughters to visit Father Ed's new parish that she hadn't yet seen. He was at a country parish in Ryan now, and the day and the area was beautiful. They spent the day chatting and laughing as if they had forever. Arlene was still wearing her headband. Nobody talked about the tests that Arlene had already been through. The cancer was in her lung and very aggressive.

Arlene could not go to work that autumn. She had surgery, she had chemotherapy and lost her hair. Rose watched her daughter go from one horrific step to the next, her heart breaking. Arlene visited her as often as she always had, but now Jake drove. She had lost her license after the first seizure, but she continued with one treatment after the next. Next month would be better. What if there was a cancer breakthrough in the next months? It could happen. Sometimes, Rose could almost believe it when there was a good day, a good week.

An agonizing year went by. The massive treatments were beginning to show. Rose's bright, optimistic daughter, her sunshine girl was slower, sometimes confused, and confessed once, that she was so tired it took all she could do to act like she was 'okay'. Rose prayed as hard as she had ever prayed in her life.

The following October, Elmer's son Pat married Julie Kielpinski. The reception at the KC hall in Standish would be a huge Polish wedding with lots of food and music and beer.

"Her immunity is nothing after all that chemo," Jake said when they visited Rose before the wedding. "She shouldn't be around a crowd like that."

"I want to go," Arlene said stubbornly. Rose looked at her daughter's pale face and knew that her daughter was dying.

Rose turned to pour the coffee, so they could not see her face. "Then I think she should go," she said to Jake, and her voice was firm. What difference would it make after all? She didn't cry until they left.

The wedding was as big as Jake had known it would be, and Arlene came under the watchful eyes of Jake and her sons. She put on her best face, smiling and talking as if the devastating disease hadn't left their mark on her. The family brought tidbits from the buffet for her that she couldn't eat, they tried their best to match her smiles and small talk, but she was wan and pale and puffy from medications, a husk of the competent school secretary, an echo of the aunt, sister, mother, friend she had always been. She had to leave early. She tired easily now. Rose stayed until Marylou took her home, but the big, happy celebration had deflated.

In November, Jake took Arlene to Standish hospital. She was so weak she couldn't feed herself anymore. The family tried to feed her, but Arlene couldn't eat. Two days later they transferred her to St. Mary's in Saginaw. She lapsed into a coma. This time Rose never doubted the outcome. She spent the days there, the evenings there. They watched the nurse's faces and lived on the thread of Arlene's own life; a good day– She was quiet, peaceful. A bad day; She tossed restlessly, babbling incoherently.

"Mom, you've got to go home. Get some rest." What did they know? Her sunshine daughter needed her, the baby Vick was excited over after eight years of no babies. Rose never forgot that he had fed the pigs and milked the cows in her last weeks of pregnancy. "She'll be a blessing when you need help," he had said. She had been. And now Arlene needed her mother. Rose would not go home.

They watched the nurses flit in and out of the room adjusting tubes and scratching unintelligible notes on her chart. Arlene was having a bad night. The nurse suggested that someone in the family stay the night. They all stayed. Day was breaking when the crisis seemed to pass, and Marylou drove Rose home with a promise that they would go back to the hospital as soon as she put in her day at school.

Rose didn't even lay down when the phone rang. "Jake just called, Mom," Marylou said. "Arlene's worse again. I'm going back to the hospital."

"Come and pick me up," Rose ordered.

Marylou didn't argue.

By evening, they abandoned the waiting room and stood by Arlene's bed. They could hear each breath in the silent room, a fight, a fight to take one more breath. The silences between each stretched longer and longer. Rose still stood waiting for the next one when Jake and Marylou started crying and the nurse came in. Jake bent over and kissed Arlene's still lips. It was over then. How could she leave this room? How could she go on and on and on? Marylou's arm came around her, and she took the first step away from the bed.

After Arlene's death, Rose felt like nothing was left. She wouldn't think of her blackout at Arlene's wake and Dorothy putting a cool cloth on her forehead and the prescriptions for her heart she had to take after that. She wouldn't think of Arlene's funeral in the Twining Baptist church that comforted Jake and her grandsons. Jake's minister had been at the hospital in Arlene's last days, a good man. It had to be all right. Acceptance was hard, but life was as life was, and family was family. They were Baptists and she was not. What difference did it make after all? The family had all turned out differently than she had expected, life had turned out differently than she had expected.

XL

What is precious is never to forget
The essential delight of the blood drawn from ageless springs...
Never to allow gradually the traffic to smother...
the flowering of the spirit.

~ MALCOLM LOWRY

1990: Another Reunion year. Rose looked forward to the Reunion with the family, which somewhere along the way the family decided would happen every other year. This summer would be especially important. Father Ed celebrated forty years in the priesthood, and Rose was going to Poland with Marylou. She went to the doctor and got her prescriptions filled, she went to Denise's Beauty Barn and got her hair done, and she went to the courthouse and got a passport. Marylou was relentless with her list of details, but Rose complied. Poland!

The reunion was barely put away when the day arrived to leave for the country her father knew in his first years, a country she could only imagine. The airport personnel were wonderful. They put her in a wheelchair (Rose felt a little uncomfortable with that—she might be slow, but she could still walk) and whisked her from one gate to another. They checked her and Marylou's passport and put them on the plane before anyone else. Although Rose was a little embarrassed, Marylou teased her that she may as well be in the company of a queen, and from now on, they would travel together. Rose had to laugh at her preferential treatment that took ninety years of life to get.

Poland echoed with a resonance of her childhood. The lush, rolling countryside, the busias leading their cows home in the evening, the rollicking sound of the polka, the solemn dimness of Polish Catholic cathedrals was like some long-ago tale that echoed in her memory, half told, half remembered. The language she had repressed for years was now all around her, and the tour guide patiently tried to teach Marylou simple words in Rose's native tongue.

They attended mass at Czestohowa, and Rose watched in awe as a silver screen opened to the sound of trumpets to reveal the venerated image of the Mother of Poland. After Mass, a priest guided them through the maze of courtyards and led them to an altar and offered them Communion. Rose sank to her knees on the cement step, her mind and heart singing, "I received communion at Czestohowa."

The winter after her trip to Poland, Rose decided to stay home for the winter. She had spent the last two winters at Marylou's, but she had hosted a party for her oldest son's 40th anniversary in the priesthood, she had traveled overseas. She certainly could stay in her own house and remember to put wood in the stove. She could hardly hear now and had to buy a stronger hearing aid, and she knew her memory was not what it had been. It drove her crazy when she couldn't find a bill or a letter, or when Tom or Marylou came over and reminded her that she didn't do this or she forgot to do that. Tom came over too often and Marylou left little notes on the table with reminders, picked up her laundry and brought her homemade bread. Father Ed came to visit her every week, and she still cooked supper for him. She was okay. They didn't need to hover.

Nevertheless, the following winter, Rose agreed to stay yet another winter at Marylou's. She didn't want to stay anywhere else but in her own space, but Father Ed kept edging both her and

Marylou into that arrangement, and perhaps it was a good thing. It was nice to have constant heat and not worry about putting wood in the stove, and she could go back to the farm in the spring.

In March of 1992, she was already looking forward to the day she could convince Marylou spring had arrived when Alice's daughter, Sue Cipolla, left a message on Marylou's answering machine while Marylou was still at work, a message that hit her like a thunderbolt. Alice had died alone and wasn't found until five days later. When Marylou sank into the couch beside her and stumbled over the awful news, Rose could not believe it. She remembered Alice's small rented home in detail– the front porch, the back yard, the small table where they shared so many meals together. Alice had heart valve surgery a few years before and laughed that it was a pig valve, but she never told them she was worried about her health. She was only concerned that her early retirement as a parapro in a local school didn't give her enough to live on. Perhaps their last trip to California should have been a warning bell. Sue and Marylou had spent hours with Alice and got her enough disability to survive.

"I tried to call her," Marlou sobbed. "For the last five days, I kept trying to call her and she wouldn't answer."

Sue was as devastated as Rose and Marylou were. Sue's brother, Jim, had put in an appearance, more angry than grief-stricken and, after a violent argument, left Sue to clean out Alice's house and make arrangements. Rose was heart-sick over her grandchildren's wounded separation. Alice's only family beyond her reach hurting each other, and she could do nothing to help. All she could do was pray.

A 'proper funeral' was out of the question, given the state of the body. Alice had talked before about cremation, but Sue had no idea what to do. Marylou told her to say a prayer, order a cremation, and asked Sue to send her sister's remains home.

The evening after Marylou's decision, she said, "I've got to run to the store, Ma. Father Ed's coming tomorrow and I forgot to pick up something for dinner." Rose still cooked for Father Ed's visits, but Rose saw that Marylou kept the meal choices simple to prepare.

"You go do what you've got to do," Rose said. "I'm not going anywhere."

After Marylou left, Rose sat in the gathering spring twilight praying for her bruised family across the continent. She didn't know how long she had been sitting there when Marylou came in and went across the living-room down the hall without a word. Probably going to change her school clothes, Rose thought. Funny she hadn't brought in any bags of groceries though.

A while later, Marylou pushed the door open with a couple of sacks of groceries and dumped them on the kitchen counter. She switched on the light. "It's getting dark, Ma. Do you want me to turn on the TV?"

"I thought you already came in," Rose said.

"Guess not," Marylou said and started unloading the groceries into the refrigerator.

"Then it was Alice," Rose said.

Marylou stopped. "What?"

"She was just here. She walked across the floor and down the hall. I thought it was you."

Marylou stared at her.

"You think I'm crazy," Rose said. She almost thought she was crazy herself.

Marylou came in and sank on the couch. "No, I don't think you're crazy. I wish I would have been here. She's telling us she's okay."

When Alice arrived in a box several days later, the box wasn't sealed too well, and Rose never told anyone that she saw that some of her daughter's remains leaked out the seams on to Marylou's kitchen counter. 'I'm glad she's okay," Rose thought. Alice's sad remains were almost more than she could bear.

In spite of Marylou's brave attempt at rescuing her sister's remains, she had no idea what was to be done with the box on her counter, but Nancy and Dorothy knew that Rose had to put her long-distance daughter to rest with the blessing of the church. They arranged a memorial mass at Saint Mark's in Au Gres and the ladies of the parish served up the usual hospitable meal after the service. Tom dug a shallow hole at the family's grave site at Omer's Catholic cemetery and Alice was put to rest.

Rose at Marylou's, last picture taken.

IXL

—O remember
In your narrowing dark hours
That more things move
than blood in the heart.

~ Louise Brogan

The summer of 1994, Rose decided that there would be one more reunion at the farm with her in command. She made lists, she ordered groceries for Marylou and Nancy to pick up, but somehow Tom and Nancy and Marylou took over in spite of her lists. Marylou came over and cleaned and Tom set up outdoor tables and games and the whole family came, and none knew about the things on her lists that she wanted fixed or painted or hidden. They brought food, they played games, they took pictures, they argued politics. The family reunion swept on and Rose was happy. She took a step down off the sun porch and the she fell and everything went black. It was only for an instant, Rose thought, and she told them she had only stumbled when she recovered on the sun porch rocker. The family pretended to agree with her, but she knew she would not be left alone again.

In the next years, Dorothy and Bob Bush died, part of her family as surely as her own children. But Rose lost her enthusiasm for having a family reunion, all those empty places in the family circle. Cancer was the new plague, even more relentless than the horrible tuberculosis that had taken her mother and aunt years ago.

In spite of her family's hovering, in spite of the family's losses, Rose kept living, and the family kept coming up with interesting diversions. She made a trip to Tennessee with Marylou and her daughter, Annette, and her great-grandkids. She had never been South before and the Smoky Mountains were as good as Tom's country songs said they were. On their way back from that trip in a driving rain, the car made an ominous clunking sound and Annette, who was driving, pulled to the side of the road.

"A flat tire," she said. At least they hadn't gotten in an accident, Rose thought. Cars were undependable and could put you in a ditch with no warning whatsoever. Before she could say her thoughts aloud, as well as her prayers for mercy, a truck pulled up behind them and a man jumped out.

"Need some help?"

After Marylou and Annette unearthed the spare tire under a mountain of luggage in the trunk, the man quickly changed the tire, and Rose insisted on giving the reluctant knight twenty dollars for his rescue.

"I didn't need to pay him, but it was only right," Rose said when they were on the road again. "He was the angel I prayed for."

"I'm glad you prayed, Grandma," Annette said.

"God always answers our prayers," Rose said. "Sometimes he says no. I'm glad this time he said yes."

The next year she went to Maine with Marylou and her son, Paul and Paul's kids. As old as she was and as hard as the trip was to see whales in the Atlantic, she loved it, although her legs swelled on the trip home and Paul and Marylou worried about her as if she would drop dead fastened in her seat belt. She knew that these trips were coming to an end.

The next year Paul suggested that they should arrange a trip somewhere in Michigan. Grandma would still travel, but would be close to home if medical help was needed. Rose was happy. As old as she was, Paul recognized her itchy traveling foot that Roseanne had scratched back in 1953. Marylou's whole family, and some family friends took Rose to the Upper Peninsula's Munising. They rented a huge building, meant to accommodate up to 24 fishermen or snowmobilers. The grandkids dubbed it the Pole Barn.

Paul and the boys caught fish, and then fried them to a crisp brown perfection. As she watched her grandsons take their turn in the kitchen, she had to wonder how different it was only one generation ago. Neither Vick nor Rose's own sons had ever known their way around a kitchen like these young ones.

Rose hadn't thought to bring anything to read, and the place didn't have any stray magazines. Cindy Pula, Annette's best friend and part of the Pole Barn crew, lent her a book (fiction!), but it was something to read, and Rose found herself enjoying the story as if it was a book from her beloved Miss Lindsey's scanty book collection years ago. But she had to take it home to finish it because there was a lot to see that week.

Cindy, a nurse and acquainted with Rose's embarrassment over using the collapsible wheelchair the family had insisted on bringing, put her in the thing and pushed her from one scenic spot to another, and Rose's embarrassment turned to gratitude when she saw waterfalls she couldn't have walked to with her cane. She saw Lake Superior that she once remembered her dad telling her about when he was working as a lumberjack and walked the shore, crying because he was so lonely, and his tears froze on his face. She had never seen the great Gitchee Gumee before. Maybe Vick was right when he had said to Gert, "If I see Michigan, that will be enough."

EPILOGUE

The falling into sleep, restfully, ever the
falling into sleep, dream, dream, and
every morning the sun comes, the sun.

~ James K. Baxter

"Are you recording that?" Mom remembered to ask me somewhere in our last recorded conversation. Sometimes a yes, sometimes a no. And then she would forget about it again.

"Would you change anything in your life if you had to do it over again?" I asked.

Mom smiled. This must be the end of the interviews. "No, I wouldn't," she said. "I just might make some mistakes that would be worse than the ones I made. You know, everybody could write two books about their life, one good and one bad. But I've had a good life. All the barn-raising bees, the neighborhood picnics; neighbors always got together. We even made a party out of picking huckleberries."

She chuckled. "The bad thing about living so long is the world moving so fast. I can't figure out how to use your telephone or how to get stations on your TV. I can't even figure out how to open my bottle of pills." Then she sobered. "The worse thing is that everyone your own age is gone. All my brothers, Dora, Gert (She died a year after Vick with a stroke). I get lonesome sometimes, but I'm never really lonely. It's funny, isn't it? I still want to live as long as God lets me. I still enjoy life."

"If you could have been anything else in life, what would you be?" I prompted.

"A writer—maybe a teacher."

All the letters she had written to friends and relatives over the years, all the journals she had filled, her letters to the editor that she had been so happy to see in print.

"You were," I said.

A silence stretched over all the stories, all the questions, all the memories. "I had a dream about your dad," she finally said. "I had it more than once." The years rolled away, and she forgot about me and the tape recorder and about the snowy cold outside. "I was sitting on a rocker and holding a baby. The baby was dressed in a snowsuit, but your dad was dressed like it was summer. He had on a yellow shirt and a straw hat, sitting kind of sideways and perky on his head. He was young and good-looking like when we were first married. He was building me a house."

"Building you a house?"

"Yes, someplace he's building me a house."

❧ ❧ ❧

The year after her Munising trip, Rose fell from a broken hip. But this time it was different from the day that Grandma Anna fell in the same way. A tall, lanky, red-haired surgeon at Bay Medical strode into the waiting room like a Cowboy hero. "I'll do surgery tomorrow and she'll be up and walking again in a few weeks," he assured me. Sure enough, she was up in a walker several weeks later. Hospice health care not only got her up and walking, they revived her weak right arm, so she tried to write again.

But the following winter she got pneumonia and was back in the hospital. The pneumonia was worse than the broken hip. She couldn't get up again. Doctor Casten ordered her moved to long term care until and unless she was no longer bedridden. I brought in the kitty I had adopted and told her that the kitchen had new cupboards. The family came in and pinned notes and pictures on the board by her bed. She was there for over a year, yet always determined that she had to get up and rejoin the family. She finally had to give up the body that wouldn't get up on June of 1999 on the night of a full moon.

ACKNOWLEDGEMENTS

I thank my son, Jim, who read my first draft and encouraged me to pursue a greater vision than the small scrapbook story that I had.

I thank MidMichigan Writers who pointed me toward a narrative that could encompass the story I was struggling to tell, especially Donnie Boursaw who researched my family's history that clarified details that I did not have from my mother's stories.and Chris Lucka, who painstakingly edited every line and gave me invaluable suggestions for filling in the timeline and enriching the story.

Finally, I thank the Arenac County Historical museum and Bay County libraries and websites for historical details.

No writer writes alone. Thank you all.

APPENDIX A

The following is one recipe of Mom's that includes a legend that she told and I've told my children and my grandchildren every time I make chicken noodle soup.

ROSE'S CHICKEN NOODLE SOUP

❧ ❧ ❧

Cut up one chicken and simmer the back, neck and all the parts you don't want to use for fried chicken. Cut five stalks celery, two onions and six carrots in small pieces. Set aside. When chicken is tender, take out pieces and peel meat from the bones.

While the chicken cooks, make noodles with five cups of flour, a dash of salt, eight eggs and a bit of cooking oil. Knead and roll out as thin as possible, cut into strips and drop into boiling chicken broth. Add cup-up vegetables and cook fifteen-twenty minutes. Stir in meat from chicken and salt and pepper to taste.

❧ ❧ ❧

Here's the story Mom told, an old legend I remember every time I eat chicken soup.

Once upon a time a poor old lady made chicken soup just as I told you. She was ready to sit down and eat when there was knock on the door. When she opened it, a man, weary and dirty from long miles of traveling, stood there. He asked if she had anything at all for him to eat, if only a crust of bread. The old lady took pity on him and invited him in and shared her soup with him. When he was finished, he thanked her and said he didn't know how to repay her, but he took out his change purse and gave her a dollar for each little fat bubble that floated on the soup's surface. Since the old lady was poor and so were her chickens, the fat globules that floated on her soup were small but many, and so the man gave her many dollars.

The old lady was overwhelmed with gratitude at her good fortune and told her neighbor about the kind man. The neighbor had seen the nondescript character in the village and would never have guessed he had so much money to give away. The next day she followed the old lady's recipe, and made soup as well. But her chickens were as fat as she was, and to be sure her broth would be even better than her neighbor's, she added an extra scoop of chicken fat from the last chicken she had cooked.

Sure enough, the poor man arrived at her door and asked if she had anything for him to eat. The neighbor lady proudly served him her chicken soup, all the while telling him that he was so lucky to have come to her door, since she was the best cook in town. When the man finished, he thanked her for her hospitality and said that he didn't know how to repay her, but again he offered to pay her for each fat bubble that floated on the soup. Unfortunately, the soup was so laden with chicken fat that the whole surface was one big bubble and the greedy lady received one dollar.

In Mom's story, the traveler was Jesus.

APPENDIX B

'ORAL HISTORY' TRACES LIVES OF THE TROMBLEYS

By Rose Trombley

Originally printed in the Bay City Times May 4th, 1986

It is surprising how we seem to be related to the human family, if not by blood ties, then by association, memories or identical names, etc.

During some discussions, I found that people are not so much interested in family trees, as they are in the folk stories. The older folks revive memories, and the younger one wonder about roots and where and how they fit in.

We sometimes do not stop to realize that there are happenings and discoveries going on in the world around us and history is being made. We read about things in the paper and then in a while, forget about it.

As for relationships, one of our daughters in California noticed a familiar name in the telephone book. She remembered her dad mention the name when she was a little girl. Just for fun, she copied the address, got in the car and went hunting. She knocked on the door. Sure enough, this was her dad's cousin Wilfred, who used to live in New York. A career change caused him to move to California. They had a wonderful visit.

I thought about the familiar names in the family stories in last year's "Families" and how they relate to me and my family {This is a reference to a series of people relating their family histories that ran in the Bay City Times over several weeks}. There are Archambeaus, Brissetts, Dishaws, Fourcheaus, who were parishioners at St. Anne's church, Linwood in the 1920's. There were Derosias and Reeds, parishioners in St. Edward's church, Omer in 1932 when we moved to Arenac County.

My aunt married a Morin, whose name I don't remember, but he had a brother named Alfred, and they named their son Alfred, who was my cousin. He died in Bay City in the summer of 1985.

My family history, as well as my husband's, is so intertwined that it's practically one story. The research for the authentic family histories on both sides of the family has been going on for two or three years now by a niece and a cousin. So I'll omit that part and just tell what was told to me and what I remember.

Of our great-grandparents, one great grandmother came to America on my father's side and my husband's great-grandfather came from France to Canada. He married an Indian maiden.

His son, my husband's grandfather, married a quadroon and moved to Detroit. He got a job, bought some acreage where Grosse Pointe is now. He did not like Detroit and did not like his job, so he got drunk with a friend one time, traded his land for a 'Democrat' buggy and a horse, loaded his possessions and his wife and came to Bay City where he claimed he had relatives.

He and his wife had five sons and two daughters. Frank, the oldest, worked on the lakes. He fell overboard and was never found. Adolph, my husband's father, married Anna Nowak, worked in lumber camps and yards, then bought a farm. Victor was a boat builder. Other children were Peter, Jerome, Amelia who married James Glancy and Mary who married William Bartlett.

My husband's grandparents on his mother's side came from the German side of Poland, where my grandparents also came from. They arrived in America the same year, 1881, at different times and landed at different places.

My relatives landed in New York and my husband's landed in Boston, Massachusetts. My father and my mother-in-law were both 11 years old at the time. They came from different directions, but arrived in Bay City, got jobs and after earning some money, bought 40-acre farms close together in Beaver Township. Both my father and my mother-in-law went to school for one year while their fathers worked in Bay City.

When they moved to the farm, they worked together and played together. All nearby farmers had some cows and there were no fences so the cattle roamed freely all through the section of woods. The leader cows wore bells, so when the children went after the cows they listened for the bells. The cows generally stayed close together.

More people kept moving in. There were no churches, no schools, no mail coming in. There were no stores. At first they had to go to Bay City to buy things they needed and later they went to Auburn. The roads wee rough and in the spring the road by our place was impassable, so the neighbor living on the side toward town had to use his team to bring whatever the other neighbors needed.

He would bring the wagon to a bad spot and another wagon would come from the other side and they would transfer the load by carrying bags across on their backs. They would lay logs with planks or boards across so they could walk across without sinking in the mud.

Flour, salt, sugar, oatmeal and cornmeal was bought by the barrel or 100-pound bags. The people did not get to church very often. Christmas and Easter were 'a must' no matter the weather. People did not have horses at first so they had to walk nine or ten miles. One Christmas, my mother-in-law said that the children would have frozen if it hadn't been for my grandfather. The children wanted to lie down and sleep, but Grandpa had them slapping their hands, stamping their feet and made them run. They got to the church early. It was dark and the church was locked, so they stayed in the entrance waiting for the church to open.

It was not until the 1880's that there was sort of a church building era. A missionary priest traveled all through northern Michigan and served all the little settlements. He would stay at someone's home, teaching, hearing confessions and having masses. In our area he always stayed at my mother-in-law's folks because it was the largest home. He encouraged people to build their own church so they sacrificed and everyone did what they could. They donated the lumber and their labor and what money they could to provide the things they could not make.

The first St. Valentine's Church in Beaver was built in 1888. The priest from Bay City would come and have mass every two weeks. Later Fisherville's St. Anthony Church was built and a pastor installed to serve both parishes.

By this time, both my father and mother-in-law left home. He went to work in the lumber camps and she went to Bay City and worked in a boarding house, where she met her husband. My father bought a 40-acre farm next to his brother's farm. My father married Josephine Sczygiel of Fisherville in 1900. I was born December 11, 1901. My father continued working out. He and his brother cooperated in supporting the two families.

When I grew up, I often wondered if they ever had disagreements when I saw how many brothers and sisters squabble over nothing. One time I asked my father and he said he didn't know if he could share with his other brothers and sisters as he did with his older brother. He said since they were children, his older brother had always looked after him and always helped him when he needed help. So he always trusted his older brother.

So with farming, my uncle had one horse, so my father bought one. He bought all the things the families needed, and the farm produce was divided.

I was the oldest, 7, and had three brothers, Walter, 5, Victor, 3, and Joseph, 18 months when my mother died on Dec. 20, 1908. My father continued working out, but now he was drilling for coal. Later he bought a rig for himself, but drilling for coal soon stopped so he was drilling wells for people—first in Flint and then closer to home.

My grandmother took care of us until my father remarried in 1910. I had seven half-sisters and three half-brothers. Leo lived on the homestead and died in January, 1975. Verna married Edward Michalski, and Tillie married George Club. Teresa married Elmer Tackman. Tillie and Teresa are twins and they all live in Bay City.

Helen married Eric Kopanka and they live in Detroit. Clara married Joe Miks, lived in Brighton and is deceased. Delphine, Eleanor and Frankie died when they were only a few months old. Albert Swiecicki lives on Midland Road.

All of us attended Cherry Hill District No. 2 after we moved across the road. Oxbow School District No. 1 was our first school. We also attended the Catholic school for a time, which was held in the church building during the week until the present brick building was completed in 1909.

My husband's family and my family attended the same school. I was excused from school a lot for two years due to my stepmother's illness, and my husband was excused because he and his brother had to help provide for the family after their father died in 1907.

My mother-in-law married Adolph Trombley Aug. 28, 1891. They had five children: James, Jerome, Gertrude, Beatrice and my husband Victor who was born Feb. 21, 1895. James died when he was only a few months old. Jerome and my husband had to help with the farming and in the winter they sawed bolts which their mother hauled to the mine.

Jerome was drafted and served in World War I. He died in the service July 18, 1918. Gertrude joined the Red Cross. She married Floyd Kingsland in 1919.

The armistice was signed Nov. 11, 1918. When the news came out, people went wild. Factory whistles blew, church, school and dinner bells were ringing, farmers were shooting their guns in the air. My father did not have any shells for his gun so he shot off some dynamite. People were whistling, singing and yelling and when the soldiers came marching home, it started all over again. Women came out of the factories with their special work uniforms and marched along with the soldiers. My cousin was among them and said, "We were in the service too."

This was the year of the great flu epidemic. People were dying, church bells tolling, bodies taken straight to the cemetery with no services because people could not congregate.

My husband's sister Beatrice was the youngest in the family, born Feb. 3, 1900. She married Leo Reinhart Aug. 28, 1920 and died Feb. 23, 1946.

I married my husband Victor Trombley Sept. 11, 1922. My maiden name was Rose Josephine Swiecicki.

We had eight children:

Jerome Edward, born July 13, 1923, now a Catholic priest serving St. Patrick's Church, Ryan and St. Francis Home, Shields.

Roseanne, born Feb. 8, 1925, married Robert Bush of Grand Rapids in August, 1960, died May 23, 1973.

Lillian, born May 1, 1926, died Jan. 20, 1946, in an automobile accident.

Elmer, born July 7, 1927, married Dorthea Badour of Standish, Sept. 12, 1954.

Alice, born Dec. 23, 1930, married Joseph Cipolla of California, Feb. 24, 1954.

Arlene, born May 27, 1938, married Jacob Dewald of Au Gres, died Nov. 29, 1983.

Mary Lou, born Feb. 10, 1942, married Dale Bugh of Standish, June, 1960.

Thomas, born June 19, 1943, married Nancy Holmberg of Allen Park, Oct. 23, 1973. They built a new home on the farm, which they now own and I still live in the old house.

I now have 20 grandchildren, with five carrying on the Trombley name. I have 11 great-grandchildren and a 12th expected.

APPENDIX C

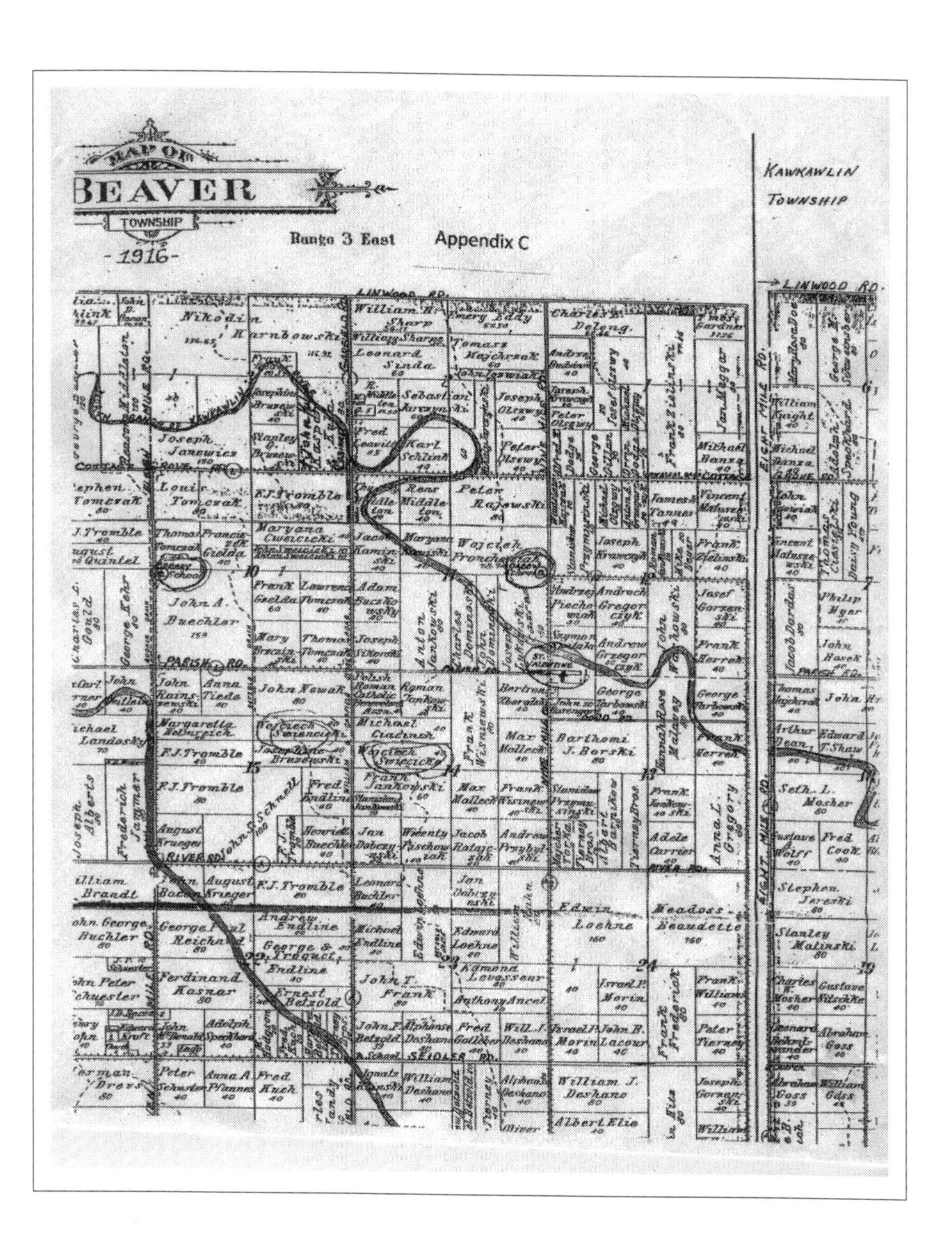

MAP OF
BEAVER
TOWNSHIP
-1916-
Range 3 East
Appendix C
KAWKAWLIN
TOWNSHIP
LINWOOD RD.
PARISH RD.
RIVER RD.
EIGHT MILE RD.
William H. Sharp
Emery Eddy
Charles R. Delong
Leonard Sinda
Sebastian Jarzynski
Karl Schlink
Peter Rajowski
Joseph Janowicz
F.J. Tromble
John A. Buechler
John Nowak
Frank Wisnewski
Barthomi J. Borski
Anna L. Gregory
Seth L. Mosher
Stephen Jerski
Stanley Malinski
Edwin Loehne
Meadoss Beaudette
William J. Deshano
Albert Elie

Made in the USA
Lexington, KY
16 June 2017